Scott Foresman - Addison Wesley

MATH

Another Look
Reteaching Masters

Grade 5

Scott Foresman - Addison Wesley

Editorial Offices: Menlo Park, California • Glenview, Illinois
Sales Offices: Reading, Massachusetts • Atlanta, Georgia • Glenview, Illinois
Carrollton, Texas • Menlo Park, California

http://www.sf.aw.com

Overview

Another Look (Reteaching Masters) provide additional teaching options for teachers to use with students who have not yet mastered key skills and concepts covered in the student edition. A pictorial model is provided when appropriate, followed by worked-out examples and a few partially worked-out exercises. These exercises match or are similar to the simpler exercises in the student edition.

For Learn lessons and Explore lessons, the masters provide an alternative approach to the lesson development. This approach simplifies or clarifies the concept presented on the student edition page.

For Problem Solving and Decision Making lessons, the masters provide additional problems with problem solving hints or problems that focus on the skills needed for the student edition lesson.

ISBN 0-201-31255-7

Copyright © Addison Wesley Longman, Inc.

Printed in the United States of America

1 2 3 4 5 6 7 8 9 10 – BW – 01 00 99 98 97

Overview

Reading Graphs

The graph on the left is called a **bar graph**.

The graph on the right is called a **pictograph**.

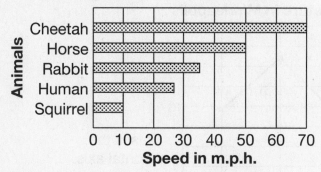

Running Speed of Land Animals

Animals: Cheetah, Horse, Rabbit, Human, Squirrel

Speed in m.p.h.
0 10 20 30 40 50 60 70

Endangered Species in the U.S.

Mammals ○ ○ ○ ○ ○ ◖
Fish ○ ○ ○ ○ ◑ ◑ ◖
Insects ○ ○

○ =10 species
◖ = 5 species

This graph shows the speeds of different animals. Look at the bar labeled "Cheetah". Line up the bar with the numbers for speed. The graph tells you that cheetahs run at ___70 m.p.h.___

This graph shows the number of endangered species in the United States. Each symbol represents 10 species. So, to find out how many species of insects are endangered, multiply 2 × 10 = ___20___.

_____

Use the graph on the left to answer **1–3**.

1. Which animal runs at about 35 m.p.h.? _____

2. Which animal on the graph is the slowest? _____

3. Which animals run faster than humans? _____

Use the graph on the right to answer **4–6**.

4. How many species of mammals in the U.S. are endangered?

_____

5. How many species of fish in the U.S. are endangered?

_____

6. How many more species of mammals are endangered than species of insects? _____

Reading Line Graphs

You can read a graph to get information. **Line graphs** show change over a period of time. This graph shows the average temperature in Minneapolis.

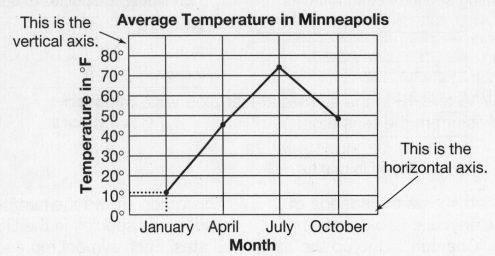

This is the vertical axis.

Average Temperature in Minneapolis

This is the horizontal axis.

What is the average temperature in Minneapolis in January?

Step 1   Find January on the horizontal axis.

Step 2   Trace a straight line from January until you reach a point on the graph. Trace another line from the point to the vertical axis to find the temperature.   __11°F__

Coordinates You can show the temperature in January by writing this coordinate: (January, 11°F). The data from the horizontal axis always goes first.

___

Use the line graph to answer **1–5**.

1. What is the average temperature in Minneapolis in April? _____

2. What is the average temperature in Minneapolis in October? _____

3. Write the coordinates to show the average temperature in July. _____

4. In which month shown is the average temperature the lowest? _____

5. Which two months have average temperatures that are about the same? _____

Reading Stem-and-Leaf Plots

A **stem-and-leaf** plot is a way to organize data. You can use it to organize the data shown.

The numbers on the left are the tens digits.

Stem	Leaf
2	3 9 5 8
1	9 8

The numbers on the right are the ones digits.

To show 19 and 18 in the stem-and-leaf plot, write the ones digit across from the tens digit, 1.

The sleeping habits of the five animals that sleep the most in a typical day are shown in the stem-and-leaf plot below. Use the stem-and-leaf plot to answer **1–4**.

Hours of Sleep

Stem	Leaf
2	2 0
1	6 9 9 ____

1. Circle the numbers that show 20 hours on the stem-and-leaf plot.

2. Suppose another animal sleeps 15 hours. Show this data in the stem-and-leaf plot.

3. How many animals sleep 20 hours? _____

4. What is the greatest number of hours shown in the table?

   _____

5. Armadillos and opossums sleep the same number of hours. The number of hours they sleep is shown in the stem-and-leaf plot. How many hours do they sleep daily?

   _____

Range, Mode, and Median

You can use data to find the range, mode, and median.

The **range** is the difference between the least and the greatest numbers.

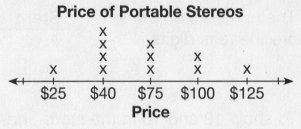

Price of Portable Stereos

What is the greatest price? __$125__

What is the least price? __$25__

greatest price – least price = __$100__

The range is __$100__.

The **mode** is the number that occurs the most.

Which price occurs most often in the plot? __$40__

This number is the mode.

The **median** is the number that is exactly in the middle, when the data is arranged in order from least to greatest.

$~~\$25~~$ $~~\$40~~$ $~~\$40~~$ $~~\$40~~$ $~~\$40~~$ $75 $~~\$75~~$ $~~\$75~~$ $~~\$100~~$ $~~\$100~~$ $~~\$125~~$

Cross off numbers on either side until you find the middle.

Which price is exactly in the middle? __$75__

This number is the median.

If there is an even number of data items, the median is exactly halfway between the two middle numbers. You can add the two middle numbers and divide by 2 to get the median.

Use the line plot to answer **1-3**.

1. What is the range? _____

2. What is the mode? _____

3. What is the median? _____

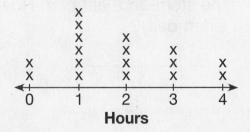

Hours Spent Reading Over the Weekend

Name _____

Introduction to the Problem Solving Guide

This graph shows the number of students who prefer different sports.

How many students did not select football or baseball?

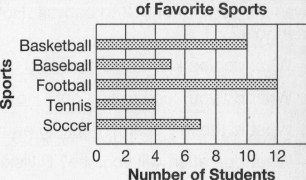

Student Survey of Favorite Sports

What do you know?

<u>The number of students who prefer each sport.</u>

What do you need to find out?

<u>The number of students who prefer sports other than football or baseball.</u>

How can you find out?

<u>Find the total number of people who prefer all the other sports.</u>

How many students picked basketball? __10 students__
tennis? __4 students__ soccer? __7 students__
Add.

__10__ (basketball) + __4__ (tennis) + __7__ (soccer) = __21__
(total not including football or baseball)

_____

1. How many more students like football than baseball and tennis combined?

   a. How many students prefer football? _____

   b. How many students prefer baseball? _____

   c. How many students prefer tennis? _____

   d. How many students prefer baseball and tennis combined? _____

   e. What is the difference between the number of students who prefer football and the number who prefer baseball and tennis combined?

   _____

Analyze Word Problems:
Choose an Operation

Joseph watched Mrs. O'Brien's children for 4 hours. He
was paid a total of $12 to babysit. How much was he paid
per hour?

What do you know? <u>He was paid $12 for 4 hours of babysitting.</u>

What do you need to find out? <u>How much he was paid an hour.</u>

What is the key action? <u>Making equal groups</u>

What operation will you use? <u>Division. $12 ÷ 4 = $3.</u>

What is the answer? <u>Joseph was paid $3 per hour.</u>

How can you check your answer?

<u>Multiply my answer by the hours he worked. The amount</u>
<u>should be the amount he was paid. $3 × 4 hours = $12.</u>

Suzanna made cookies for her school's bake sale. She
baked 2 dozen chocolate chip and 3 dozen peanut butter
cookies. How many dozen cookies did she bake in all?

1. What do you know?

_____

2. What do you need to find out?

_____

3. What is the key action? _____

4. What operation will you use? _____

5. What is the answer? _____

6. How can you check your answer?

_____

_____

Exploring Algebra:
What's the Rule?

In your book, you answered questions to find the
rule for a table. Here is another way to find the rule.

A	B
2	4
3	6
5	10
7	14
9	18

Ask yourself: "What can I do to 2 to make 4?"

$2 + 2 = 4$

$2 \times 2 = 4$

Then ask: "Which operation will work for the next pair?"

$3 + 2 \neq 6$

$3 \times 2 = 6$

To write the rule using a variable, replace the number from the
table (3) with a variable (n).

So, change 3×2 to $n \times 2$.

To write the rule in words, just describe the operation: multiply by 2.

_____

A	B
1	5
6	10
8	12
10	14
13	17

1. a. What can you do to 1 to make 5? _____

    b. Which operation will work for the next pair?

_____

    c. Write the rule using a variable. _____

    d. Write the rule using words. _____

    e. Does the rule work for all the pairs in the table? _____

Scales and Bar Graphs

Make a **bar graph** for the data in this table.

Visitors to Historic Museums in 1995	
Boot Hill Museum (Dodge City, KS)	124,000
Pioneer Arizona Living History Museum (Phoenix, AZ)	47,000
Shelburne Museum (Shelburne, VT)	155,000
St. Augustine Historic District (St. Augustine, FL)	60,000

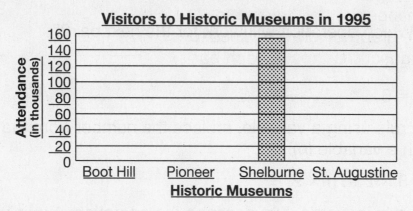

Step 1   Give the graph a title.

Step 2   Label the horizontal axis with the museum names. Label the vertical axis with a scale. Since all the data is in thousands up to 155,000, you can use numbers from 0 to 160 in thousands. Label each line in units of 20, so you can fit number up to 160 on your graph.

Step 3   Use the data in the table to draw the bar for the attendance at Shelburne. It was 155,000, so the bar should go almost to 160.

1. Complete the graph above for visitors to historic museums in 1995.

2. Follow the same steps to make a bar graph for the data in this table on a separate sheet of paper.

3. What scale will you use?

Visitors to Children's Museums in 1995	
Boston, MA	395,000
New York, NY	250,000
Portland, OR	60,000
Los Angeles, CA	250,000

_____

_____

Exploring Making Line Graphs

In your book, you explored making **line graphs**. Here is another way to make line graphs.

Use what you learned about making bar graphs to help you make line graphs.

Day of Storm	Depth of Snow (in inches)
1	4
2	6
3	5
4	8
5	10
6	9

Step 1 Make a bar graph to show the data in the table.

Step 2 Change the bar graph into a line graph by drawing lines to connect the tops of each bar.

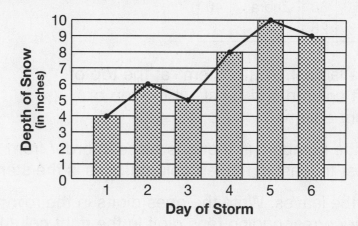

1. Make a bar graph that shows the data in the table.

2. Change the bar graph to a line graph by connecting the tops of each bar.

Day of Storm	Depth of Snow (in inches)
1	6
2	4
3	8
4	9
5	7
6	8

Exploring Making Stem-and-Leaf Plots

In your book you made **stem-and-leaf plots**. Here is another way to make stem-and-leaf plots.

The stem-and-leaf plot is like a bar graph made of numbers. It helps you see what group of numbers makes up the greatest part of the data.

Average Speed in Miles per Hour			
Cat	30	Lion	50
Cape Hunting Dog	45	Pig	11
Cheetah	70	Rabbit	35
Elephant	25	Squirrel	12
Grizzly Bear	30	Zebra	40
Human	28		

Stem	Leaf
7	0
6	
5	0
4	5 0
3	0 0 5
2	5 8
1	1 2

Step 1 Draw a large T. Write "Stem" at the top of the left column and "Leaf" at the top of the right column.

Step 2 Write the numbers in the tens place in order from greatest to least in the left column. This is the stem.

Step 3 Make the leaves. Write the ones digits in the row next to their corresponding tens digit in the right column.

---

1. Make a stem-and-leaf plot for the data in the table below.

Average Life Span in Years			
Rhinoceros (white)	20	Red Fox	7
Rhinoceros (black)	15	Guinea Pig	10
Rhesus Monkey	15	Rabbit	5
Polar Bear	20	Squirrel	10
Lion	15	Chipmunk	6
Horse	20	Giraffe	10
Grizzly Bear	25	Leopard	12
Gorilla	20	Pig	10
Dog	12	Kangaroo	7
Cat	12	Opossum	1
Camel	12	Mouse	3
Black Bear	18		

Stem	Leaf

Analyze Strategies:
Use Logical Reasoning

Alberto, Casey, Edgar, and Glenda each do best in one of four school subjects: spelling, science, reading, and math. Casey was the winner of the school spelling bee. Alberto doesn't like to read. Edgar hopes to become a scientist. Given these interests, which student likes to read.

What information is given directly? <u>Casey won the spelling bee and Edgar wants to become a scientist.</u>

Cross out spelling and science in the list of subjects.

<u>Since Alberto hates to read, the only other subject left is math.</u>

Cross out math in the list of subjects.

<u>Glenda must be the one who likes to read.</u>

_____

There are four members of different ages on the Southside Bowling Team. They always bowl according to their age, oldest to youngest. Allison is not the oldest team member. Katie bowls second. Sophie does not bowl last. Georgia is almost the youngest team member. In what order does the team bowl?

1. What information is given directly? _____

2. Who bowls second? _____

3. What clues help you rule out who bowls last?

_____

_____

4. Who bowls last? _____

5. What clue helps you decide who bowls third?

_____

6. Who bowls third? _____

7. Who bowls first? _____

Exploring a Million

In your book you used place-value blocks and grid paper to explore a million. Here's another way to understand millions.

A roll of dimes is worth $10.00. It holds 100 dimes. How many dimes are there in 5 rolls?

$10 — Dimes — $10 ◯ $10 — Dimes — $10 ◯ $10 — Dimes — $10 ◯ $10 — Dimes — $10 ◯ $10 — Dimes — $10 ◯

5 rolls of 100 dimes each is the same as 5 hundreds or __500 dimes__.

50 rolls of 100 dimes each is the same as 50 hundreds or
5 thousands or __5,000__.

500 rolls of 100 dimes each is the same as 500 hundreds or
50 thousands or __50,000__.

5,000 rolls of 100 dimes each is the same as 5,000 hundreds or
500 thousands or __500,000__.

50,000 rolls of 100 dimes each is the same as 50,000 hundreds or
5,000 thousands or 5 millions or __5,000,000__.

_____

How many dimes are in each number of rolls?

1. 8 rolls = _____ rolls of 100 dimes = _____ hundreds = _____ dimes

2. 12 rolls = _____ rolls of 100 dimes = _____ hundreds = _____ dimes

3. 20 rolls = _____ hundreds = _____ dimes

4. 87 rolls = _____ hundreds = _____ dimes

5. 120 rolls = _____ hundreds = 12 thousands = _____ dimes

6. 370 rolls = _____ hundreds = _____ thousands = _____ dimes

7. 700 rolls = _____ hundreds = _____ thousands = _____ dimes

8. 1,600 rolls = _____ hundreds = 160 thousands = _____ dimes

9. 5,000 rolls = _____ hundreds = _____ thousands =

   _____ dimes

10. 20,000 rolls = _____ hundreds = 2,000 thousands =

   _____ millions = _____ dimes

Name _____

Exploring Adding and Subtracting Decimals

In your book you used place-value blocks to add and subtract decimals. Here is another way to add and subtract decimals.

You can use money to show decimals.

$$\begin{array}{r} 3.27 \\ + 1.35 \\ \hline \end{array}$$

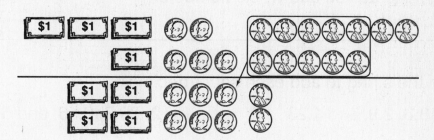

You can exchange 10 of the pennies for another dime.
So, 3.27 + 1.35 = 4.62.

Use place-value blocks or money to find each sum or difference.

1. $\begin{array}{r} 3.12 \\ + 1.29 \\ \hline \end{array}$

2. $\begin{array}{r} 4.51 \\ - 1.41 \\ \hline \end{array}$

3. $\begin{array}{r} 4.62 \\ + 1.39 \\ \hline \end{array}$ **4.** $\begin{array}{r} 6.51 \\ + 2.36 \\ \hline \end{array}$ **5.** $\begin{array}{r} 4.89 \\ - 3.76 \\ \hline \end{array}$ **6.** $\begin{array}{r} 8.91 \\ - 5.02 \\ \hline \end{array}$

Name _____

Adding Decimals

You can use a string of decimal points to help you add decimals.

To add 4.6, 13 and 0.67, write the numbers
so that the decimals are on the string.
Write whole numbers to the left of the string.
Then add as you add whole numbers.

```
 4.6
13.
 0.67
─────
18.27
```

Use the string to add each set of decimals.

1. 3.6, 2.9, and 1.23

2. 23.7, 0.56, and 5.3

3. 41.75, 15.1, and 5

4. 0.90, 0.09, and 9.09

Find each sum.

5. $6.39 + $1.19 = _____

6. 0.25 + 1.6 + 2.9 = _____

7. 4.29 + 0.06 = _____

8. 6.91 + 11 + 1.2 = _____

9. 3.6 + 0.14 = _____

10. 4.69 + 3.1 + 7 = _____

Subtracting Decimals

You can use place-value blocks to help you
subtract decimals.

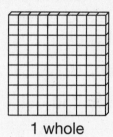

1 whole   1 tenth   1 hundredth

1.25 − 0.16

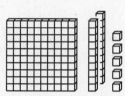

First subtract the hundredths. Since you
cannot take 6 from 5 you must regroup.
Regroup 1 tenth as 10 hundredths.

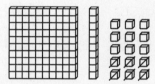

15 hundredths − 6 hundredths = __9__ hundredths

Subtract the tenths.

1 tenth − 1 tenth = __0__ tenths

Subtract the ones.

1 one − 0 ones = __1__ one

$$\begin{array}{r} {\scriptstyle 1\ 15} \\ 1.2\!\!\!/5 \\ -\ 0.1\ 6 \\ \hline 1.0\ 9 \end{array}$$

Use place-value blocks to help you find each difference.

1. 2.35 − 1.41 = _____

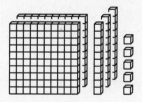

2.	6.8	**3.**	2.3	**4.**	6.9 4	**5.**	8.0 0
	− 1.7		− 0.6 5		− 0.0 7		− 1.3 5

Name _____

Analyze Word Problems:
Choose an Operation

Jan and Bobby went bowling on a Saturday afternoon. Bobby's scores were 98, 134, and 125. Jan's scores were 112, 208, and 99. Who had the greater total score?

What do you know? You know their scores.

What do you need to find out? You need to find out whose total score was greater.

Decide what operation makes sense. Write number sentences to find Bobby's and Jan's total scores. To find a total of two or more numbers, add.

Bobby's scores $98 + 134 + 125 =$ __357__

Jan's scores $112 + 208 + 99 =$ __419__

Since __419__ > __357__, Jan's score was greater.

Write a number sentence to solve each problem. Then solve the problem.

1. Marcia and Peter traveled 366 miles on their first day of vacation. The second day they traveled 486 miles. How many miles had they traveled all together?

2. Karen and Sue run 2 miles every day. Karen has run 486 miles. Sue has run 366 miles. How many more miles has Karen run than Sue?

3. June read a 576-page book one week and a 328-page book the next. How many pages did she read in all?

Exploring Multiplication Patterns and Properties

In your book, you explored multiplication patterns and properties. Here is another way to understand properties.

Commutative Property When you commute from home to work by train or car, the distance you go back and forth is the same. The distance stays the same, no matter the order.

$$10 \times (2 \times 10) = 10 \times (10 \times 2) = 200$$

Associative Property When an association meets members can group themselves in different ways. The association stays the same.

$$10 \times (10 \times 2) = (10 \times 10) \times 2 = 200$$

You can use properties to make solving $4 \times (7 \times 25)$ easier.

$4 \times (7 \times 25)$ Use the commutative property to change the order. $\rightarrow$ $4 \times (25 \times 7)$

$4 \times (25 \times 7)$ Use the associative property to change the grouping. $\rightarrow$ $(4 \times 25) \times 7$

$(4 \times 25) \times 7 = \underline{\;\;100 \times 7\;\;} = \underline{\;\;700\;\;}$

Find each product. Use multiplication properties.

1. $(7 \times 5) \times 40 =$

    $7 \times (\underline{\quad\quad} \times \underline{\quad\quad}) =$

    $7 \times \underline{\quad\quad\quad} = \underline{\quad\quad}$

2. $100 \times (30 \times 7) =$

    $(100 \times \underline{\quad\quad}) \times \underline{\quad\quad} =$

    $\underline{\quad\quad\quad} \times 7 = \underline{\quad\quad\quad}$

3. $8 \times (10 \times 3) = \underline{\quad\quad\quad}$

4. $30 \times (40 \times 5) = \underline{\quad\quad\quad}$

5. $50 \times (4 \times 2) = \underline{\quad\quad\quad}$

6. $(8 \times 70) \times 10 = \underline{\quad\quad\quad}$

Name _____

Estimating Products

To estimate a product, you can round before you multiply.
Look at these two examples.

	Round	Use Mental Math	Estimate
398 x 18	4<u>00</u> x 2<u>0</u>	4 x 2 = 8	8,<u>000</u>
398 x 99	4<u>00</u> x 1<u>00</u>	4 x 1 = 4	4<u>0</u>,<u>000</u>

Estimate the product. Round. Then use mental math.

1. 7 × 37

7 × 40 = _____

2. 8 × 74

8 × 70 = _____

3. 89 × 6

_____ × 6 = _____

4. 63 × 170

_____ × 200 = _____

5. 22 × 99

_____ × 100 = _____

6. 38 × 41

40 × _____ = _____

7. 59 × 78

_____ × _____ = _____

8. 198 × 61

_____ × _____ = _____

9. 33 × 34

_____ × _____ = _____

10. 102 × 48

_____ × _____ = _____

Multiplying Whole Numbers

Find the product: 56×23

You can use place value to help you multiply whole numbers. Break up whole numbers to make them easier to multiply mentally. Pair the pieces of each number and multiply.

$56 = 50 + 6$

$23 = 20 + 3$

$$\begin{array}{r} 50 + 6 \\ \times\ 20 + 3 \end{array}$$

$3 \times 6 = 18$

$3 \times 50 = 150$

$$\begin{array}{r} 50 + 6 \\ \times\ 20 + 3 \end{array}$$

$20 \times 6 = 120$

$20 \times 50 = 1,000$

Find the sum of all the partial products.

$120 + 18 + 1,000 + 150 = \underline{\ 1,288\ }$

$56 \times 23 = \underline{\ 1,288\ }$

Complete each problem.

1. 28×87

   a. $28 = 20 + 8$

      $87 = 80 + 7$

      $7 \times 8 = \underline{\hphantom{XXXXXX}}$

      $7 \times \underline{\hphantom{XXXX}} = \underline{\hphantom{XXXX}}$

         $20 + 8$

      $\times\ 80 + 7$

      $80 \times 8 = \underline{\hphantom{XXXXXX}}$

      $80 \times \underline{\hphantom{XXXX}} = \underline{\hphantom{XXXX}}$

   b. Find the sum of all the partial products. _____

   c. $28 \times 87 = \underline{\hphantom{XXXXX}}$

2. $\begin{array}{r} 3\,7 \\ \times\ 4\,2 \\ \hline \end{array}$

3. $\begin{array}{r} 5\,9 \\ \times\ 2\,3 \\ \hline \end{array}$

4. $\begin{array}{r} 4\,3\,8 \\ \times\ \ \ 6\,3 \\ \hline \end{array}$

5. $\begin{array}{r} 8\,5 \\ \times\ 5\,3 \\ \hline \end{array}$

Distributive Property

The distributive property lets you break up numbers before you multiply.

To multiply 2×126, break 126 into $120 + 6$.

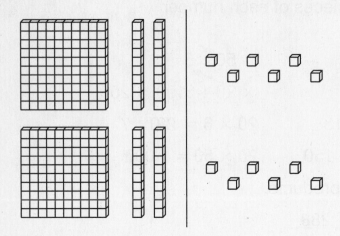

$$2 \times 126 = 2 \times (120 + 6)$$
$$= (2 \times 120) + (2 \times 6)$$
$$= \quad 240 \quad + \quad 12$$
$$= \quad \underline{252}$$

Complete each problem.

1. $3 \times 18 = 3 \times (\underline{\quad} + \underline{\quad})$
$$= (3 \times \underline{\ }) + (3 \times \underline{\ })$$
$$= \underline{\quad} + \underline{\quad}$$
$$= \underline{\quad}$$

2. $253 \times 4 = 4 \times (\underline{\quad} + \underline{\quad})$
$$= (4 \times \underline{\ }) + (4 \times \underline{\ })$$
$$= \underline{\quad} + \underline{\quad}$$
$$= \underline{\quad}$$

3. $404 \times 2 = 2 \times (\underline{\quad} + \underline{\quad})$
$$= (\underline{\ } \times 400) + (2 \times \underline{\ })$$
$$= \underline{\quad} + 8$$
$$= \underline{\quad}$$

4. $8 \times 128 = 8 \times (\underline{\quad} + \underline{\quad})$
$$= (\underline{\ } \times \underline{\ }) + (8 \times 8)$$
$$= 960 + \underline{\quad}$$
$$= \underline{\quad}$$

Choosing a Calculation Method

Using different calculation methods for different problems
will save you time. Before you multiply, think about which
method is best for each problem.

Use mental math

- for problems with zeros 400×50

- for problems with numbers
  near benchmarks 199×20

- for short problems 22×7

- for easy problems 15×6

Use a calculator

- for problems with large numbers $928{,}640 \times 741{,}306$

- for difficult problems $84{,}996 \times 5{,}588$

- when you want the exact answer quickly 14×15

Use paper and pencil
$$\begin{array}{r} 7\,3\,5 \\ \times\ \ 2\,6 \\ \hline \end{array}$$

- the rest of the time

What method would you use to solve each problem? Circle one.
Then solve, using that method.

1. $302 \times 84 =$ _____

mental math
calculator
paper and pencil

2. $74 \times 20 =$ _____

mental math
calculator
paper and pencil

3. $\begin{array}{r} 6\,7{,}9\,8\,9 \\ \times\ \ \ \ 7\,8\,7 \\ \hline \end{array}$

mental math
calculator
paper and pencil

Exploring Patterns with Multiples

In your book you used patterns to explore multiples.
Here is another way to explore multiples. On this grid,
multiples of 2 are shaded and multiples of 3 are crossed.

1	2	3	4	5	6	7	8	9	10
11	12	13	14	15	16	17	18	19	20

Common multiples are multiples that are shared by two or
more numbers. The common multiples of 2 and 3 are 6, 12,
and 18. Each common multiple of 2 and 3 is circled on the
grid above. The least common multiple (LCM) of 2 and 3 is 6.

Use this grid to help you answer **1–4**.

1	2	3	4	5	6	7	8	9	10
11	12	13	14	15	16	17	18	19	20
21	22	23	24	25	26	27	28	29	30
31	32	33	34	35	36	37	38	39	40

1. Shade the multiples of 4.   **2.** Cross the multiples of 5.

3. What are the common multiples of 4 and 5 on the grid? _____

4. What is the least common multiple of 4 and 5 on the grid? _____

Use this grid to help you answer **5–8**.

1	2	3	4	5	6	7	8	9	10
11	12	13	14	15	16	17	18	19	20
21	22	23	24	25	26	27	28	29	30
31	32	33	34	35	36	37	38	39	40
41	42	43	44	45	46	47	48	49	50
51	52	53	54	55	56	57	58	59	60

5. Shade the multiples of 6.   **6.** Cross the multiples of 8.

7. What are the common multiples of 6 and 8? _____

8. What is the least common multiple of 6 and 8? _____

© Scott Foresman Addison Wesley 5

Name _____

Decision Making

Sanur is buying dinner for himself and two friends. Jane wants salad, juice, and a veggie burger. Chas wants juice and a hamburger but no salad. Sanur wants salad and a hamburger, but a different kind of juice than Jane and Chas.

Menu			
	Small (Serves 1)	**Medium** (Serves 2)	**Large** (Serves 3)
Hamburger	$3.00		
Veggie Burger	$3.50		
Salad	$1.00		$2.50
Juice	$0.75	$1.25	$1.50

1. Who can share juice? _____

2. Will anyone share salad? _____

_____

3. What will Sanur buy? _____

_____

4. How much will it cost? Show the cost of each item.*

_____

5. If everyone wanted a hamburger, salad, and the same juice, what would Sanur buy?

_____

6. How much would this cost? Show the cost of each item.

_____

7. What is the difference between the two costs?

_____

Exploring Decimal Patterns

In your book, you used a calculator to explore patterns.

You can use place-value patterns to find the product of a decimal and a power of ten. Whole numbers that end in 0 are a power of ten.

Find 2.5×100.

Which number is a power of 10? __100__

To multiply a decimal by a power of ten, count the number of zeros at the end of the power of ten. How many are there? __2__

Move the decimal point over that same number of places, adding a zero if necessary.

$2.5 \times 100 = 2.5 = 2.50 = $ __250__

Find each product.

1. $3.4 \times 1,000$

    a. Which number is a power of ten? _____

    b. How many zeros are in that power of ten? _____

    c. How many places should you move
    the decimal point to find the product? _____

    d. Write the product. _____

2. $5.2 \times 100 = $ _____

3. $4.7 \times 1,000 = $ _____

4. $3.83 \times 10 = $ _____

5. $1.76 \times 1,000 = $ _____

6. $4.52 \times 100 = $ _____

7. $8.6 \times 1,000 = $ _____

8. $9.103 \times 100 = $ _____

9. $5.387 \times 1,000 = $ _____

10. $1.54 \times 100 = $ _____

11. $3.265 \times 1,000 = $ _____

12. $0.25 \times 100 = $ _____

13. $0.700 \times 1,000 = $ _____

14. $0.1 \times 100 = $ _____

15. $2.43 \times 1,000 = $ _____

16. Find the product of 6.0253 and 1,000. _____

Estimating Decimal Products

You can use a number line to estimate products.

Estimate 28 × 7.36.

First round 28 to the nearest ten.

Look at the digit right of the tens digit. 2<u>8</u>

28 rounds to 30 because 8 is greater than 5.

On the number line you can see that 28 is closer to 30 than to 20.

Round 7.36 to the nearest one.

Look at the digit right of the ones digit. 7.<u>3</u>6

7.36 rounds to 7 because 3 is less than 5.

On the number line you can see that 7.36 is closer to 7 than to 8.

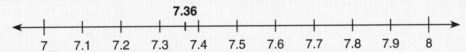

Multiply the rounded numbers to find the estimate of the product.

30 × 7 = __210__

The estimated product of 28 and 7.36 is __210__.

_____

Estimate each product.

1. 4.3 × 31

   a. Round 31 to the nearest ten. _____

   b. Round 4.3 to the nearest one. _____

   c. Find the product of the rounded numbers. _____

2. 4.85 × 23 _____   **3.** 48 × 3.16 _____

4. 97.8 × 59 _____   **4.** 3.6 × 47 _____

5. 67.7 × 49 _____   **6.** 2.6 × 26 _____

Multiplying Whole Numbers
and Decimals

You can use place-value blocks to help you to multiply decimals.

2.43×3

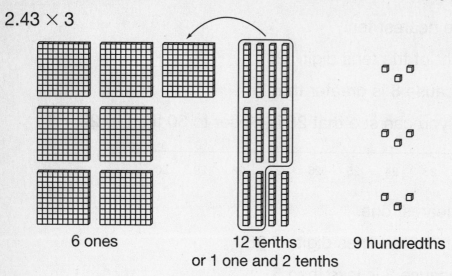

6 ones   12 tenths   9 hundredths
or 1 one and 2 tenths

Count the blocks in each place. Regroup when necessary.

$2.43 \times 3 = 7.29$

Find each product. You can draw place-value blocks to help.

1. $3.13 \times 4 =$ _____   **2.** $3 \times 1.25 =$ _____

3. $16.95 \times 5 =$ _____   **4.** $20 \times 4.03 =$ _____

5. $7.49 \times 27 =$ _____   **6.** $6 \times 8.51 =$ _____

7. $18 \times 1.45 =$ _____   **8.** $17.11 \times 5 =$ _____

9. $4.72 \times 39 =$ _____   **10.** $7 \times 2.24 =$ _____

11. $7 \times 10.36 =$ _____   **12.** $5.06 \times 9 =$ _____

13. $12 \times 12.04 =$ _____   **14.** $6.43 \times 11 =$ _____

Analyzing Word Problems:
Multiple-Step Problems

Nadia is planning to grow tomatoes. She needs 2 packs of seeds and 2 stakes. Packs of tomato seeds are $1.19 each and stakes are $0.50 each. What will be the total cost of her garden project?

Understand

What question do you need to answer?
   How much will 2 packs of seeds and 2 stakes cost.

Plan

What is the cost of 1 pack of tomato seeds? $1.19

How much will 1 stake cost? $0.50

Solve

Step 1   Find the cost of 2 packs of seeds. $2 \times \$1.19 = \$2.38$

Step 2   Find the cost of 2 stakes. $2 \times \$0.50 = \$1.00$

Step 3   Find the total. $\$2.38 + \$1.00 = \$3.38$

Solve each problem.

1. Nadia plants 6 large tomato plants and 5 cherry tomato plants. There are 12 tomatoes on each large tomato plant and 22 tomatoes on each cherry tomato plant. How many tomatoes does she have in all?   _____

2. Nadia sold 66 of her large tomatoes for $0.50 each and 100 of her cherry tomatoes for $0.05 each.

   a. How much money did she earn?   _____

   b. How many tomatoes does she have left?   _____

3. Next time Nadia grows tomatoes, she plans on buying plant food, which costs $4.29 a pack. If she buys 3 packs and a watering can for $3.79, how much will she spend?

   _____

Exploring Decimal Multiplication

In your book, you used grids to find decimal products.
Here is another way to multiply decimals.

Find 0.3 of 0.5.

Make an array using dimes and pennies.

Make one row of 3 dimes and one
column of 5 dimes.

Make an array of pennies next to the dimes.

Count the pennies. Write the amount
using a decimal.

0.3 of 0.5 is ___0.15.___

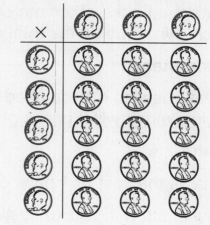

Use dimes and pennies to help you find each product.

1. 0.8 of 0.3

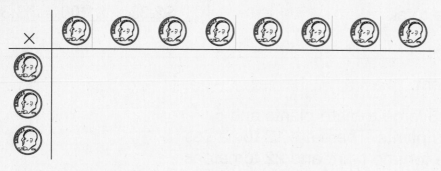

   a. Draw pennies to complete the array.

   b. How many pennies are there? _____

   c. 0.8 of 0.3 is _____.

2. 0.4 of 0.5

   a. How many dimes will you need? _____

   b. How many pennies are in the array? _____

   c. 0.4 of 0.5 is _____.

3. 0.3 of 0.7 is _____.   **4.** 0.2 of 0.8 is _____.

5. 0.4 of 0.4 is _____.   **6.** 0.9 of 0.3 is _____.

Multiplying Decimals by Decimals

For each product, write the decimal point in the correct place.

$3.45 \times 2.5 = 8625$

Find the number of decimal places in the factors. 3.45×2.3

__2__ decimal places + __1__ decimal place = __3__ decimal places

Place the decimal point in the product 3 decimal places from the right.

$3.45 \times 2.5 =$ __8.625__

Follow the same steps to write the decimal point in the correct place for each product.

1. 21.6×0.8

    a. ____ decimal place(s) + ____ decimal place(s) = ____ decimal places

    b. $21.6 \times 0.8 = 1\,7\,2\,8$

2. 0.04×8

    a. ____ decimal places + ____ decimal places = ____ decimal places

    b. $0.04 \times 8 = 3\,2$

3.	4.	5.	6.
5.0 8 × 0.4	7 0.5 × 0.0 2	1.3 4 2 × 2.7	9.0 8 × 0.0 4

7.	8.	9.	10.
6.5 3 × 1.9	7.4 8 × 1.0 3	8.8 7 × 0.5	2.2 3 5 × 1.7

11. Check your answer to **4.** Explain why it is different from the others?

_____

_____

Finding High and Low Estimates

You can use high and low estimates to find the range of a
product before multiplying.

85.79×3.3 **A.** 110 and 240   **B.** 255 and 280   **C.** 240 and 360

Between which two numbers will the product be found?

For a low estimate, use the first digit of each number.
Change remaining digits to 0.

$80 \times 3 =$ __240__ Low Estimate

For a high estimate, increase the first digit by 1.
Change remaining digits to 0.

$90 \times 4 =$ __360__ High Estimate

The range for 85.79×3.3 is __240__ to __360__.

The product will be found between 240 and 360.

Between which two numbers will each product be found?

1. 3.2×7.79 **A.** 37 and 73   **B.** 10 and 21   **C.** 21 and 32

     Low estimate: _____   High Estimate: _____   Answer: _____

2. 8.93×9.7 **A.** 17 and 79   **B.** 72 and 90   **C.** 93 and 97

     Low estimate: _____   High Estimate: _____   Answer: _____

3. 6.73×71.2 **A.** 420 and 560   **B.** 240 and 650   **C.** 130 and 240

     Low estimate: _____   High Estimate: _____   Answer: _____

4. 4.7×6.94 **A.** 12 and 16   **B.** 24 and 35   **C.** 24 and 30

     Low estimate: _____   High Estimate: _____   Answer: _____

5. 12.3×4.8 **A.** 48 and 52   **B.** 16 and 48   **C.** 40 and 100

     Low estimate: _____   High Estimate: _____   Answer: _____

Decimals and Zeros

Multiplying decimals is similar to multiplying whole numbers.
The only difference is placing the decimal point.

0.6×0.002

Step 1   Count the decimal places.

0.6		0.002		product
1 number after the decimal point	+	3 numbers after the decimal point	=	4 numbers after the decimal point

Step 2   Multiply as with whole numbers. Add zeros to the
left of the product to give enough digits before the
decimal point.

$6 \times 2 = 12$

$0.6 \times 0.002 = \underline{\ \ 0.0012\ \ }$

Find each product.

1. 0.08×0.006

   a.   0.08   0.006   product

   ____ numbers after   +   ____ numbers after   =   ____ numbers after
     the decimal point   the decimal point   the decimal point

   b. $8 \times 6 =$ _____

   c. $0.08 \times 0.006 =$ _____

2. $\begin{array}{r} 0.0\,7 \\ \times\ \ \ 0.7 \\ \hline \end{array}$ **3.** $\begin{array}{r} 1.6 \\ \times\,0.0\,0\,2 \\ \hline \end{array}$ **4.** $\begin{array}{r} 0.0\,1 \\ \times\,0.0\,1 \\ \hline \end{array}$ **5.** $\begin{array}{r} 0.0\,5 \\ \times\,0.0\,2 \\ \hline \end{array}$

6. Check your answer to question **5**. Does it follow the
rule? Why or why not?

_____

_____

Analyzing Strategies:
Guess and Check

A store manager is planning a 100-hour work schedule for the week. The manager schedules 6-hour and 8-hour long shifts. There will be two more 8-hour shifts than 6-hour shifts. How many shifts for each time period will there be?

You know that there are 6-hour and 8-hour shifts. Altogether the shifts must total 100 hours.

Make a guess for the number of 6-hour shifts. You know there will be 2 more 8-hour shifts.

	6-hour shifts	8-hour shifts	Total hours
Guess 1:	2	4	$(2 \times 6) + (4 \times 8) = 44$–too low
Guess 2:	8	10	$(8 \times 6) + (10 \times 8) = 128$–too high
Guess 3:	5	_7_	$(5 \times 6) + (\underline{\ 7\ } \times 8) = \underline{\ 86\ }$ –too low
Guess 4:	6	_8_	$(6 \times 6) + (\underline{\ 8\ } \times 8) + \underline{\ 100\ }$.

The first guess is too low. Try a greater number for your second guess.

The second guess is too high. Your next guess should be between two and eight 6-hour shifts.

The schedule will have __6__ 6-hour shifts and __8__ 8-hour shifts.

---

1. Together, Stephanie and Jane have saved $65.50 towards buying a new telescope. Jane has saved $9.50 more than Stephanie. How much did each contribute? Use the table to help you organize your guesses.

	Stephanie's Contribution	Jane's Contribution	Total
Guess 1:	$10.00	_____	$10.00 + _____ = _____
Guess 2:	$30.00	_____	$30.00 + _____ = _____
Guess 3:			
Guess 4:			

Stephanie contributed $_____ and Jane contributed $_____.

Reviewing the Meaning of Division

You can use counters to help you divide.

Find 20 ÷ 4.

Place 20 counters on your desk.

You have 20 counters. You need to divide them into groups of 4.

How many groups of 4 are there? __5__

So, 20 ÷ 4 = 5.

Find each quotient. Use counters to help.

1. 24 ÷ 8

    a. Draw counters in the space to
    the right to show 24 counters
    divided into groups of 8.

    b. How many groups of
    8 counters are there? _____

    c. 24 ÷ 8 = _____

2. 15 ÷ 3 = _____

3. 42 ÷ 6 = _____

4. 36 ÷ 9 = _____

5. 64 ÷ 8 = _____

6. 12 ÷ 2 = _____

7. 21 ÷ 7 = _____

Exploring Patterns to Divide

In your book you used a calculator to find division patterns.
Here is another way to use patterns to divide.

Use the basic fact $12 \div 2 = 6$ to help you divide
larger numbers.

12 tens $\div 2 = 6$ tens

$120 \div 2 = 60$ There is one zero in the dividend and no zeros in
the divisor. Place one zero in the quotient.

12 hundreds $\div 2 = 6$ hundreds

$1{,}200 \div 2 = 600$ There are two zeros in the dividend and no zeros in
the divisor. Place two zeros in the quotient.

12 thousands $\div 2 = 6$ thousands

$12{,}000 \div 2 = 6{,}000$ There are three zeros in the dividend and no zeros
in the divisor. Place three zeros in the quotient.

You can use basic facts and patterns to divide
larger numbers.

_____

Use patterns and basic facts to divide.

1. $36{,}000 \div 4$

    a. Basic fact: $36 \div 4 =$ _____

    b. Add one zero to the end of the quotient: $360 \div 4 =$ _____

    c. Add two zeros to the end of the quotient: $3{,}600 \div 4 =$ _____

    d. $36{,}000 \div 4 =$ _____

2. $1{,}800 \div 6$

    a. What basic fact will you use to help find the answer? _____

    b. $1{,}800 \div 6 =$ _____

3. $250 \div 5 =$ _____   4. $1{,}400 \div 7 =$ _____

Estimating Quotients

Estimate 172 ÷ 3.

To estimate a quotient, just look at the first two digits of the dividend. Think: 15 ÷ 3 = 5, so 17 ÷ 3 is close to 5 and 170 ÷ 3 is close to 50.

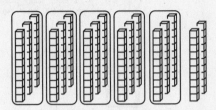

Since 170 ÷ 3 is about 50, a good estimate for 172 ÷ 3 is about 50.

Estimate.

1. 316 ÷ 5

    a. 31 ÷ 5 is about _____.

    b. How many zeros should you add to the quotient? _____

    c. A reasonable estimate for 316 ÷ 5 is _____.

2. 436 ÷ 8

    a. _____ ÷ 8 is about _____.

    b. How many zeros should you add to the quotient? _____

    c. A reasonable estimate for 436 ÷ 8 is _____.

3. 297 ÷ 4

    a. _____ ÷ 4 is about _____.

    b. 297 ÷ 4 is about _____

4. 655 ÷ 7

    a. _____ ÷ 7 is about _____.

    b. 655 ÷ 7 is about _____

5. 195 ÷ 6 _____   **6.** 237 ÷ 7 _____

7. 509 ÷ 9 _____   **8.** 714 ÷ 8 _____

Name _____

Exploring Dividing

In your book you used play money to solve division problems. Here is another way to divide money.

Divide $4.28 by 3.

Divide the dollars by repeated subtraction. How many groups of 3 dollars can you take away? __1__

Change any dollars that are left to dimes.

Divide the dimes by repeated subtraction. How many groups of 3 dimes can you take away? __4__

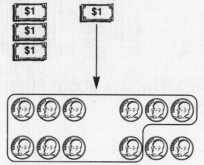

Change any dimes that are left to pennies.

Divide the pennies by repeated subtraction. How many groups of 3 pennies can you take away? __2__

How many pennies are left over? __2__

Write the quotient using a dollar sign and a decimal point.

$4.28 ÷ 3 = 1 group of dollars, 4 groups of dimes, 2 groups of pennies, and 2 pennies left over.

$4.28 ÷ 3 = $1.42 R2

Find the quotient.

$6.16 ÷ 5

1. How many groups of 5 dollars can you make? _____

2. How many groups of 5 dimes can you make? _____

3. How many groups of 5 pennies can you make? _____

4. How many pennies are left over? _____

5. Write the quotient. _____

50 Use with pages 176–177.

Dividing by 1-Digit Divisors

4$\overline{)257}$

You can use place-value blocks to divide.

Step 1   Use place-value blocks
to show 257.

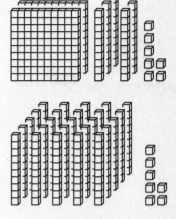

Step 2   Since you cannot divide the
hundreds blocks into four
equal groups, regroup the
hundreds as tens.

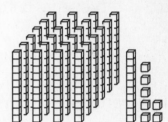

Step 3   Divide the tens into four equal groups.

Step 4   Regroup the left over tens as ones.

Step 5   Divide the ones into four equal groups.

Step 6   Find the number in one group.

6 tens + 4 ones = 60 + 4 = 64 $\dfrac{64 \text{ R1}}{4\overline{)257}}$

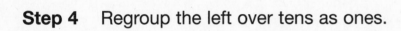

Use place-value blocks to divide.

1. 7$\overline{)582}$

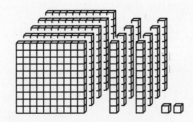

2. 9$\overline{)428}$

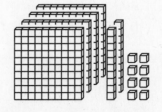

Analyze Word Problems:
Interpret Remainders

Tia went to the book closet to get notebooks for her class of 32 students. The notebooks are packed 6 to a carton. How many cartons does she need?

You know that each carton holds 6 notebooks. Tia needs to get enough cartons for 32 students.

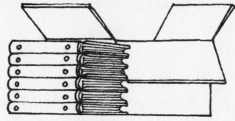

You can draw a picture to help you solve the problem. Each carton represents 6 notebooks.

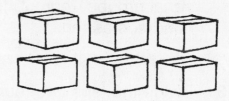

Are 5 cartons enough? $5 \times 6 = 30$
No, 2 more notebooks are needed.

$$\begin{array}{r} 5\ \text{R2} \\ 6\overline{)32} \\ -30 \\ \hline 2 \end{array}$$

Are 6 cartons enough? $6 \times 6 = 36$ __Yes__ .

In the lunchroom, students sit at tables of 6. There are 82 students eating lunch. How many tables must be set up?

1. How many students sit at 1 table? _____

2. Draw a picture to show the number of tables needed.

3. How many tables are needed? _____

4. How many of the tables will be full? _____

5. At the right, show the division problem you could use to solve the problem.

Deciding Where to Place the First Digit

When you divide, how do you find where to place the first digit of your quotient? You can estimate the answer or you can try the following approach.

Look at the first digit of the dividend. Is it equal to or greater than the divisor? If so, begin writing your answer above the first digit of the dividend.	$\begin{array}{r} 123 \\ 3\overline{)369} \end{array}$
If the first digit of the dividend is less than the divisor, begin writing your answer above the 2nd digit of the dividend.	$\begin{array}{r} 89 \\ 3\overline{)267} \end{array}$

Decide where to place the first digit of your answer. Then solve the problem.

$$\begin{array}{r} 214 \\ 2\overline{)428} \end{array}$$

Where does the quotient's first digit go? Explain.

  In the hundreds place because the 4 in 428 is greater than the divisor.

1. $4\overline{)484}$

   a. Where does the quotient's first digit go? Explain.

   _____

   _____

   b. Find the quotient. _____

2. $6\overline{)372}$

   a. Where does the quotient's first digit go? Explain.

   _____

   _____

   b. Find the quotient. _____

Zeros in the Quotient

3)626

You can use place-value blocks to show division.

Step 1 Show 626 with place-value blocks.

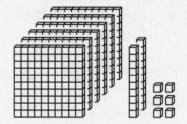

Step 2 Divide the hundreds into
3 equal groups.

How many hundreds are
in each group? If there are
any hundreds left over,
regroup them as tens.

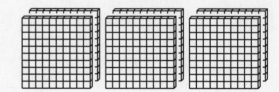

Step 3 Since you cannot divide the
tens into three equal groups,
regroup the tens as ones.

Step 4 Divide the ones into three equal groups.

How many ones are in each group? __8__

How many ones are left over?. __2__

2 hundreds + 8 ones = 200 + 8 = 208

626 ÷ 3 = __208 R2__

Use place-value blocks to divide.

1. 4)412

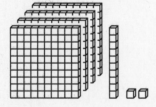

2. 3)628

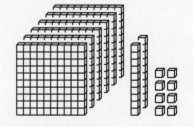

3. 7)1,428   **4.** 6)31,520   **5.** 5)303

Exploring Mean

In your book you used estimates to explore mean. Here is another way to understand the mean.

Find the mean, median, and mode for this set of data.

7, 7, 10, 11, 7, 6, 8

	6
	7
	7
	7
	8
	10
	+ 11
	56

Step 1   Order the numbers from least to greatest.

Step 2   To find the **mean**, find the sum of the numbers.
Then divide by the number of addends.
There are 7 addends, so divide by 7.
$56 \div 7 = 8$
The mean is __8__.

Step 3   To find the **median**, find the number
in the exact middle of the list. There
are 3 numbers on either side of 7,
so the median is __7__.

	6
	7
	7
	⑦
	8
	10
	+ 11
	56

Step 4   To find the **mode**, look for the number
that occurs most often. Since there
are three 7s, the mode is __7__.

Find the mean, median, and mode of each set of data.

1. 4, 7, 9, 11, 4

   a. Write the numbers in order from least to greatest. _____

   b. Find the sum of the numbers. _____

   c. How many numbers are in the set? _____

   d. mean: _____ ÷ _____ = _____

   e. median: The middle number is _____.

   f. mode: The number that occurs the most is _____.

2. 61, 42, 67, 61, 45, 33, 55   **3.** $26, $21, $19, $16, $23

   a. mean: _____   **a.** mean: _____

   b. median: _____   **b.** median: _____

   c. mode: _____   **c.** mode: _____

Name _____

Exploring Products and Quotients

In your book you explored products and quotients by
testing examples. Here is another way to remember facts
about products and quotients.

Factor	Factor	Product
n	1	n
> 1	> 1	> either factor
n	0	0

Dividend	Divisor	Quotient
n	1	n
> 1	> 1	< dividend
0	n	0

Look for clues in the factors. Complete using >, <, or =.

1. 4 8 ⟶ factor is ◯ 1

    × 5 ⟶ factor is ◯ 1

    product is ◯ either factor

2. 4 9 8 ⟶ factor is ◯ 1

    × 1 ⟶ factor is ◯ 1

    product is ◯ the first factor

3. 9 2 7 ⟶ factor is ◯ 1

    × 0 ⟶ factor is ◯ 0

    product is ◯ 0

4. 7 9 ⟶ factor is ◯ 1

    × 8 ⟶ factor is ◯ 1

    product is ◯ either factor

5. 1)1,267

   The dividend is ◯ 1.

   The divisor is ◯ 1.

   The quotient is ◯ the dividend.

6. 56)475

   The dividend is ◯ 1.

   The divisor is ◯ 1.

   The quotient is ◯ the dividend.

Dividing Money

You can divide money in the same way that you divide whole numbers.

To divide $73.26 by 3, first find 7,326 ÷ 3.

Divide the thousands. Multiply, subtract, and compare.

Divide the hundreds. Multiply, subtract, and compare.

Divide the tens. Multiply, subtract, and compare.

Divide the ones. Multiply, subtract, and compare.

Write the dollar sign and decimal point in the answer. The decimal point goes in front of the tens digit.

$$\begin{array}{r} 2{,}442 \\ 3\overline{)7{,}326} \\ -6\phantom{{,}000} \\ \hline 13 \\ -12 \\ \hline 12 \\ -12 \\ \hline 06 \\ -6 \\ \hline 0 \end{array}$$

$73.26 ÷ 3 = ___$24.42___

Find each quotient.

1. 5)$76.15

   a. Write the whole number division problem you can solve to help you find the quotient.

   _____

   b. Find the whole number quotient.

   _____

   c. Find the money quotient.

   _____

2. 4)$65.32

3. 3)$34.41

Dividing Decimals

You can use place-value blocks to help you
divide decimals.

Find the quotient.   4)6.12

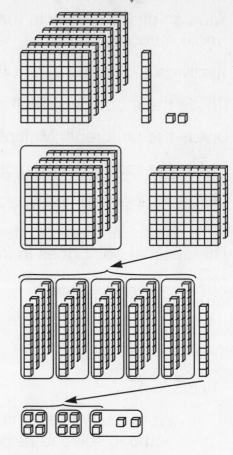

Divide the ones. How many
groups of 4 ones can you make? __1__
Exchange each of the remaining
ones for 10 tenths.

Divide the tenths. How many
groups of 4 tenths can you make? __5__
Exchange each of the remaining
tenths for 10 hundredths.

Divide the hundredths. How many groups
of 4 hundredths can you make? __3__

Count the number of groups of each
block you have and write the quotient.

1 group of ones, 5 groups of tenths, and 3 groups of hundredths
1 + 0.5 + 0.03 = 1.53

6.12 ÷ 4 = __1.53__

_____

Find each quotient. Use place-value blocks to help.

1. 5)8.85

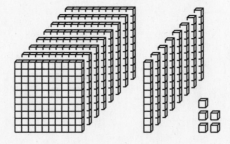

2. 3)13.2   **3.** 6)17.52

Factors and Divisibility

A factor evenly divides a given number.

You can use multiplication facts to help you find factors.

Find the factors of 18.

Look for whole numbers whose product is 18.

Start with 1.

$1 \times 18 = 18$	**1** and **18** are factors of 18.
$2 \times 9 = 18$	**2** and **9** are factors of 18.
$3 \times 6 = 18$	**3** and **6** are factors of 18.
$4 \times ? = 18$ $5 \times ? = 18$	There are no numbers that will give a product of 18 when multiplied by 4 or 5.

All the factors of 18 have been found since the factors greater than 4 and 5 are also shown in the number sentences above.

The factors of 18 are ___1, 2, 3, 6, 9, and 18___ .

___

Find the factors for each number. Write multiplication facts to show the factors.

1. 24

    a. $1 \times$ _____ $= 24$

    b. $2 \times$ _____ $= 24$

    c. $3 \times$ _____ $= 24$

    d. $4 \times$ _____ $= 24$

    e. List all the factors of 24. _____

2. 15

    a. Write all the multiplication facts that show the factors of 15.

    _____

    b. List all the factors of 15. _____

Name _____

Exploring Prime and Composite Numbers

In your book you used a hundred chart to find prime and composite numbers. Here is another way to find prime and composite numbers.

A **composite number** has more than two factors. Using counters, you can make a rectangle with more than one row.

6 is a <u>composite number</u>.
Its factors are <u>1, 2, 3, and 6</u>.

A **prime number** has only two factors. Using counters, you cannot make a rectangle with more than one row.

7 is a <u>prime number</u>.
Its factors are <u>1 and 7</u>.

_____

1. a. Form a rectangle with 21 counters.

   b. Is 21 prime or composite? _____

2. a. Form a rectangle with 23 counters.

   b. Is 23 prime or composite? _____

3. a. Form a rectangle with 35 counters.

   b. Is 35 prime or composite? _____

Write whether each number is prime or composite.

4. 18   **5.** 29   **6.** 45

_____   _____   _____

Analyze Strategies:
Work Backward

Two hours after opening, Mr. Irving's newsstand sold 18 newspapers. Half of the remaining newspapers were sold before closing. There were 10 newspapers left. How many newspapers were at the newsstand when it opened?

You can work backward from the end to the beginning. Undo each step.

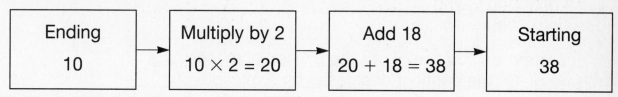

Ending	Multiply by 2	Add 18	Starting
10	$10 \times 2 = 20$	$20 + 18 = 38$	38

$10 \times 2 = 20$, $20 + 18 = 38$

So, there were ___38 newspapers___ at the store when it opened.

Work backward to solve each problem. Complete each drawing to show the steps.

1. Lucia finished her chores at 5:00 P.M. She spent 15 minutes cleaning her room and three times that amount of time washing the dishes. At what time did Lucia start her chores? _____

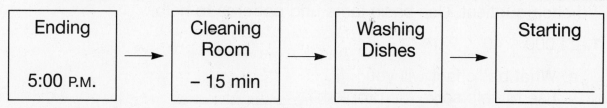

Ending	Cleaning Room	Washing Dishes	Starting
5:00 P.M.	– 15 min	_____	_____

2. Mrs. Oakley bought day-old bread from a bakery for $0.50. The bread had been marked down twice — $\frac{1}{2}$ off the first time, and $\frac{1}{2}$ off the second time. What was the original price of the bread?

_____

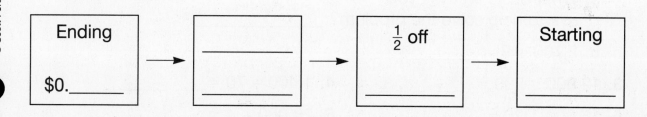

Ending		$\frac{1}{2}$ off	Starting
$0.____	_____	_____	_____

Exploring Division Patterns

In your book you used a calculator to explore division patterns. Here is another way to understand division patterns. You can use basic facts to help you divide.

Example 1

Use the basic fact $18 \div 9 = 2$ to help you divide.

$$18,000 \div 9 = 2,000$$
$$18,000 \div 90 = 200$$
$$18,000 \div 900 = 20$$

What pattern do you see? As the divisor increases by a multiple of 10, the quotient decreases by a multiple of 10.

Example 2

Use the basic fact $15 \div 3 = 5$ to help you divide.

$$15 \div 3 = 5$$
$$150 \div 3 = 50$$
$$1,500 \div 3 = 500$$

What pattern do you see? As the dividend increases by a multiple of 10, the quotient increases by a multiple of 10.

Find each quotient. Use basic facts and patterns to help.

1. $24,000 \div 40$

  a. What basic fact will you
  use to help solve the problem? _____

  b. What is the quotient of $24,000 \div 4$? _____

  c. $24,000 \div 40 =$ _____

2. $2,700 \div 9$

  a. What basic fact will you
  use to help solve the problem? _____

  b. $2,700 \div 9 =$ _____

3. $12,000 \div 300 =$ _____   **4.** $1,400 \div 70 =$ _____

5. $16,000 \div 20 =$ _____   **6.** $28,000 \div 4 =$ _____

Name _____

Estimating Quotients: High and Low

You can use basic facts to estimate quotients.

Estimate the quotient of 13,145 ÷ 50. Give a high and low estimate.

Think 13 ÷ 5.

What two basic facts could help you estimate?

13 ÷ 5 is close to the basic facts 10 ÷ 5 = 2 and 15 ÷ 5 = 3.

10 ÷ 5 = 2	15 ÷ 5 = 3
10,000 ÷ 50 = 200	15,000 ÷ 50 = 300
The low estimate is __200__.	The high estimate is __300__.

The exact quotient is __between 200 and 300__.

_____

Estimate each quotient. Give a high and low estimate.

1. 23,093 ÷ 30

   a. Name two basic facts
   that are close to 23 ÷ 3. _____

   b. Write the number sentences you will use to find the estimates.

_____

2. 3,427 ÷ 60

   a. Name two basic facts
   that are close to 34 ÷ 6. _____

   b. Write the number sentences you will use to find the estimates.

_____

3. 4,089 ÷ 70	**4.** 35,274 ÷ 40
_____	_____
5. 8,127 ÷ 90	**6.** 17,056 ÷ 80
_____	_____
7. 4,388 ÷ 70	**8.** 23,544 ÷ 70
_____	_____

Estimating with 2-Digit Divisors

You can use basic facts and compatible numbers to estimate with 2-digit divisors.

Estimate the $423 \div 21$.

Think about basic facts that could help you estimate.
(Hint: Look at the front digits of each number to help!)

$4 \div 2 = 2$

$400 \div 20 = 20$

$423 \div 21$ is about 20.

Use basic facts to estimate each quotient.

1. $898 \div 32$

   a. What basic fact could you
use to estimate the quotient? _____

   b. Write the number sentence you can use to find
the estimate.

     $900 \div 30 =$ _____

2. $3,505 \div 53$

   a. What basic fact could you
use to estimate the quotient? _____

   b. Write the number sentence you can use to find
the estimate.

     $3,500 \div 50 =$ _____

3. $316 \div 82$ **4.** $1,222 \div 38$ **5.** $8,057 \div 89$

_____   _____   _____

Dividing by 2-Digit Divisors

You can use pennies to help you divide.

Divide 122 by 21.

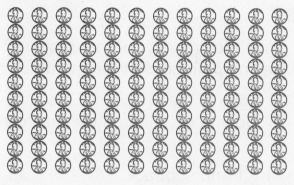

Sort the pennies into groups of 21.

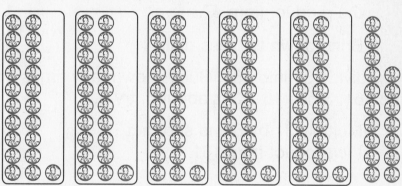

There are 5 groups of 21 pennies with 17 pennies left over.
So, 122 ÷ 21 = ___5 R17___.

Find each quotient. Use pennies or other counters to help.

1. 175 ÷ 25 = _____

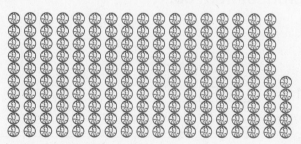

2. 248 ÷ 26 = _____

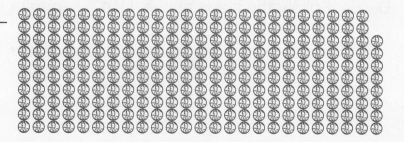

Dividing Greater Numbers

Estimation can help you divide greater numbers.

Divide $31\overline{)4,716}$

Where will you place the first digit of the quotient?
Since 31 < 47, the first digit goes in the hundreds place.

Look at the first 2 digits of the dividend. Guess how
many times 31 will go into 47. Since 3 will only divide 4
one time, try 1.

Multiply 31 by 1 and subtract
the product from 47.

$$\begin{array}{r} 3\,1 \\ \times\ \ 1 \\ \hline 3\,1 \end{array}$$

$$\begin{array}{r} 1 \\ 31\overline{)4,716} \\ -31 \\ \hline 161 \end{array}$$

Bring down the tens digit.

Now divide 31 into 161. Guess how many times 31 will go
into 161. Since 16 ÷ 3 is about 5, try 5.

Multiply 31 by 5 and subtract
the product from 161.

$$\begin{array}{r} 3\,1 \\ \times\ \ 5 \\ \hline 1\,5\,5 \end{array}$$

$$\begin{array}{r} 15 \\ 31\overline{)4,716} \\ -31 \\ \hline 161 \\ -155 \\ \hline 66 \end{array}$$

Bring down the ones digit.

Guess how many times 31 will go into 66. Since 6 ÷ 3
is 2, try 2.

Multiply 31 by 2 and subtract
the product from 66.

$$\begin{array}{r} 3\,1 \\ \times\ \ 2 \\ \hline 6\,2 \end{array}$$

$$\begin{array}{r} 152\ \text{R4} \\ 31\overline{)4,716} \\ -31 \\ \hline 161 \\ -155 \\ \hline 66 \\ -62 \\ \hline 4 \end{array}$$

$4,716 \div 31 = \underline{\ \ 152\ \text{R4}\ \ }$

Divide. Follow the steps above. Use a separate piece of
paper if necessary.

1. $23\overline{)744}$ **2.** $42\overline{)4,756}$ **3.** $38\overline{)4,196}$

Dividing: Choosing a Calculation Method

The table shows three methods for solving division.

Method	When to Use
Mental math	Solve division problems with multiples of ten or with other easy numbers.
Calculator	Solve difficult division problems.
Paper and pencil	Solve medium division problems when a calculator is not available.

Example   2,736 ÷ 76

Method: calculator

Answer: 36

Explain: Long division can be done more accurately with a calculator.

Divide and check. Tell which calculation method you used and why. Calculation methods may vary.

1. 3,600 ÷ 60

Method: _____

Answer: _____

Explain: _____

_____

_____

2. 486 ÷ 7

Method: _____

Answer: _____

Explain: _____

_____

_____

Divide and check.

3. 2,928 ÷ 61 = _____

4. 3,500 ÷ 70 = _____

5. 134 ÷ 3 = _____

6. 2,484 ÷ 46 = _____

7. 1,731 ÷ 54 = _____

8. 635 ÷ 33 = _____

Zeros in the Quotient

Sometimes a quotient has a zero in it. These examples show
how to handle zeros.

$$
\begin{array}{r}
280 \text{ R5} \\
25\overline{)7{,}005} \\
-50 \\
\hline
200 \\
200 \\
\hline
05 \\
-0 \\
\hline
5
\end{array}
$$

5 < 25
Try 0.

$$
\begin{array}{r}
302 \\
25\overline{)7{,}550} \\
-75 \\
\hline
05 \\
-0 \\
\hline
50 \\
-50 \\
\hline
0
\end{array}
$$

5 < 25
Try 0.

You need to place 0 in these quotients to show you have
no <u>ones</u> or <u>tens</u>.

Divide and check. Use the steps as a guide.

1. $7\overline{)426}$

2. $33\overline{)3{,}521}$

3. $63\overline{)6{,}847}$

4. $34\overline{)31{,}975}$

5. $56\overline{)22{,}712}$

6. $63\overline{)25{,}313}$

7. $37\overline{)39{,}513}$

8. $23\overline{)57{,}691}$

9. $17\overline{)51{,}717}$

Exploring Algebra: Using Expressions

In your book, you used algebraic expressions to represent
pictures. Here you will work with algebraic expressions
and variables.

Algebraic Expression
$n + 7$
↑
variable

$n + 7$ is an algebraic expression because it
has the variable n. A variable is a letter that
is used to represent a number.

Evaluate $n + 7$
for $n = 6$
↓
$\boxed{6} + 7 = 13$

To *evaluate* an algebraic expression means to find
its value by replacing the variable with a number.

Evaluate each algebraic expression.

1. 8   + n for $n = 9$
↓   ↓
8   + $\boxed{}$ = ____

2. 10   + n for $n = 5$
↓   ↓
10   + $\boxed{}$ = ____

3. n –   6   for $n = 13$
↓   ↓
$\boxed{}$ –   ____ = ____

4. 3   × n for $n = 8$
↓   ↓
____   × $\boxed{}$ = ____

5. n ÷   2   for $n = 18$
↓   ↓
$\boxed{}$ ÷   ____ = ____

6. n +   11   for $n = 5$
↓   ↓
$\boxed{}$ +   ____ = ____

7. n –   12   for $n = 15$
↓   ↓
$\boxed{}$ –   ____ = ____

8. n ×   5   for $n = 4$
↓   ↓
$\boxed{}$ ×   ____ = ____

Analyze Strategies:
Use Objects/Act It Out

You decide to design an apartment building in the shape
of a staircase. The tallest section will have 4 apartments.
How many apartments will be in the building? Use cubes
to represent the apartments to help solve the problem.
Build a staircase.

Step 1	Step 2	Step 3	Step 4
Start with 4 cubes.	Next, place 3 cubes.	Then, add 2 cubes.	Finally, place 1 cube.

Count the cubes to find out how
many are used to make the staircase. __10__

Since each cube represents an the apartment,
there are __10__ apartments.

Use cubes to help solve each problem.

1. Design a building in the shape of a staircase. The tallest
   section will have 7 apartments. How many apartments
   will be in the building?

   _____

2. Design a building that is in the shape of a cube. Each
   side of the building will be 2 apartments long.

   a. How many apartments are on the first floor? _____

   b. How many floors high will the building be? _____

   c. How many apartments will there be in all? _____

Name _____

Dividing Money

You can use play money or draw a money model to
help you divide money. Divide $3.84 by 12.

Step 1	Step 2	Step 3
Divide the dollars into groups of 12.	Change each of the dollars to dimes. Divide the dimes into groups of 12.	Change the 2 remaining dimes to 20 pennies. Divide the pennies into groups of 12.

There are not enough dollars to divide into groups of 12.	There are 3 groups of 12 and 2 dimes remaining.	There are 2 groups of 12.

$3.84 divided by 12 is ___$0.32___ .

Use play money or draw a picture to divide.

1. 11)$2.75

2. 10)$12.50

3. 12)$9.00

4. 27)$3.51

5. 15)$48.00

6. 30)$95.70

Decision Making

FOUR STAR CINEMA	MOVIE TIMES	Popcorn Specials
★ ★ ★ ★	**Space and Beyond** 1:00 • 3:00 • 5:00 • 7:00	★ ★ ★ ★
FOUR STAR CINEMA	**Vacation of a Lifetime** 1:30 • 3:30 • 5:30 • 7:30	Large Popcorn with 10 oz. Juice → $5.50
ADMISSION Adults $6.00 Children $3.25	**Looking for Laughter** 1:15 • 3:30 • 5:45 • 8:00	Medium Popcorn with 6 oz. Juice → $3.50
	City Under Siege 12:45 • 3:15 • 5:45 • 8:15	★ ★ ★ ★

Use the information given to answer the questions.
In all situations, assume that you must be at the theater
15 minutes before showtime.

1. If it takes 15 minutes to get to the
   movie theater, what time would you
   leave to see *Space and Beyond* at 3:00? _____

2. If it is 3:00 and you have 15 minutes to
   travel, what movies can you see?

   _____

3. What is the cost of admission for three
   adults and four children? _____

4. Is $20 enough to pay for 2 adults, 2 children,
   and a medium popcorn special? Explain. _____

5. If it takes 30 minutes to get to the theater,
   what is the latest time you can leave to
   see *City Under Siege* at 5:45? _____

6. If you arrive at the movie theater at 6:45,
   what is the earliest movie you can see? _____

7. Sarah wants to take 6 friends and her
   mother to see a movie. If all of her friends
   qualify for children's tickets, what will be
   the total cost of admission? _____

© Scott Foresman Addison Wesley 5

Exploring Decimal Patterns in Division

In your book you used a calculator to divide decimals. Here is another way to divide decimals. When you divide a decimal by 10, 100, or 1,000, the digits in the decimal remain the same, but the decimal point moves to the left.

Examples

168.3 ÷ 10	10 has **1 zero**.	Move decimal **1 place** left.

$$16.83$$

168.3 ÷ 100	100 has **2 zeros**.	Move decimal **2 places** left.

$$1.683$$

168.3 ÷ 1,000	1,000 has **3 zeros**.	Move decimal **3 places** left.

$$0.1683$$

If there are not enough digits, add zeros to the left of the number.

3.2 ÷ 1,000	Move decimal **3 places**.	Add 2 zeros.

$$0.0032$$

Circle the letter of the correct quotient.

1. 62.5 ÷ 10   **a.** 0.625   **b.** 6.25   **c.** 0.0625

2. 736.4 ÷ 100   **a.** 7.364   **b.** 73.64   **c.** 0.7364

3. 62.15 ÷ 1,000   **a.** 6.215   **b.** 0.06215   **c.** 6,215

Find each quotient. Use mental math.

4. 231.8 ÷ 100 = _____   **5.** 62.8 ÷ 10 = _____

6. 249.2 ÷ 1,000 = _____   **7.** 44 ÷ 10 = _____

8. 34.8 ÷ 100 = _____   **9.** 3,841.9 ÷ 1,000 = _____

Lines and Angles

Parallel lines always lie side by side. $\overleftrightarrow{AB}$ is parallel to $\overleftrightarrow{CD}$.

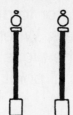

Intersecting lines cross at one point. $\overleftrightarrow{EF}$ and $\overleftrightarrow{GH}$ are intersecting lines.

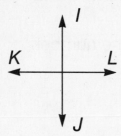

Perpendicular lines are intersecting lines that form square corners where they cross. $\overleftrightarrow{IJ}$ and $\overleftrightarrow{KL}$ are perpendicular.

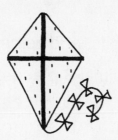

Write the name for each pair of lines.

1. _____

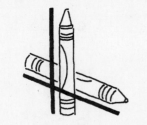

2. _____

3. _____

4. _____

Exploring Measuring Angles

In your book, you classified angles using a protractor. Here is another way.

This shelf is at a right angle to the wall. The books fit the "right" way.

This shelf is at an obtuse angle, which is larger than a right angle. The books slide to the floor.

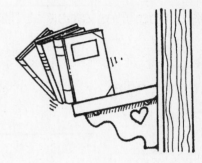

This shelf is at an acute angle, which is smaller than a right angle. The books won't fit on this shelf.

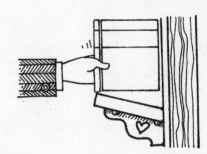

Write the name of each angle.

1. _____

2. _____

3. _____

4. _____

5. _____

6. _____

Name _____

Triangles

You can classify triangles by the lengths of their sides and the size of their angles.

acute—
all angles less
than 90°

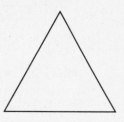

equilateral—
sides the same
length

This is an
equilateral, acute
triangle.

Not all acute
triangles are
equilateral.

right—
one right angle

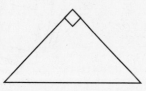

isosceles—
two sides the
same length

This is an
isosceles, right
triangle.

Not all right
triangles are
isosceles.

obtuse—
one obtuse angle

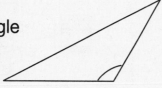

scalene—
no sides the
same length

This is a **scalene,
obtuse** triangle.

Not all obtuse
triangles are
scalene.

Classify each triangle by its sides and angles.

1. _____

_____

2. _____

_____

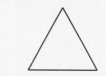

3. _____

_____

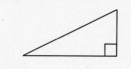

4. _____

_____

5. _____

_____

6. _____

_____

Quadrilaterals

Quadrilaterals can be classified by the lengths of their sides and the size of their angles. You can use a ruler to measure the sides and a protractor to measure the angles.

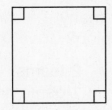

All sides are the same length.

All angles are right angles.

This figure is a **square**.

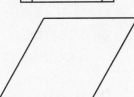

All sides are the same length.

There are two sets of parallel sides.

There are no right angles.

This figure is a **rhombus**.

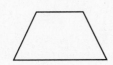

There are two parallel sides of different lengths.

This figure is a **trapezoid**.

Measure each quadrilateral. Then write its name.

1. _____

2. _____

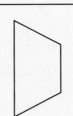

3. _____

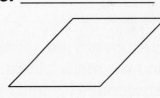

4. _____

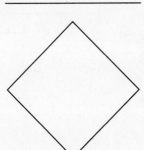

5. _____

6. _____

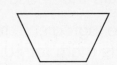

Analyze Strategies: Solve a Simpler Problem

Use a pattern to help you solve a simpler problem.

10 teams are playing in a basketball tournament. If they lose a game, they are eliminated from the tournament. How many games have to be played to find the tournament champion?

Make the problem simpler. Look at the numbers in both columns. Do you notice a pattern?

 2 teams, 1 game ringed

 4 teams, 3 games ringed

Teams	Games
2	1
4	3
6	5
8	?
10	?

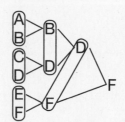 6 teams, 5 games ringed

Follow the pattern. How many games will 8 teams play? __7__

How many games will 10 teams play? __9__

---

1. 3 students are sitting on a bench eating lunch. In how many different arrangements can these students sit together?

   _____

2. The Stewart family has 4 members. They wanted to pose for a picture together. How many different ways could they pose together in a line?

   _____

3. The ingredients for 1 brownie cost $0.35. The school sells them for $0.75 each. The computer club gets $0.25 from each sale and the soccer team gets the rest. If 100 brownies are sold, how much does the soccer team get after ingredients costs and the computer club are taken care of?

   _____

© Scott Foresman Addison Wesley 5

Name _____

Similar and Congruent Polygons

Congruent polygons have the same size and shape.

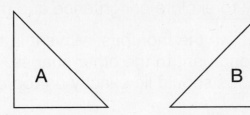

If you can't slide, flip or turn a figure to see if it matches exactly, use your ruler. If you measure two polygons and they are the same size and shape, then they are congruent.

Figures A and B both measure 1 in. by 1 in. by $1\frac{3}{8}$ in.

Figures A and B are congruent.

If two figures are the same shape, but different sizes, then they are **similar**.

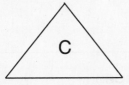

Figures C and D are the same shape, but not the same size. They are similar.

_____

1. Which polygon is congruent to ? _____

a.   **b.**   **c.**

2. Which polygon is similar to ? _____

a.   **b.**   **c.**

Exploring Congruence and Motions

In your book you explored congruence and motions with pentominoes. Here is another way to explore congruence and motions.

Trace the rhombus on the left. Cut out the rhombus. Move it in the motions described to see if it is congruent to the other shapes. To be congruent, the traced rhombus should lie exactly on top of the other shape.

 slide The 2 shapes are congruent.

 flip The 2 shapes are not congruent.

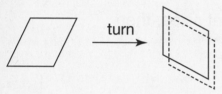 turn The 2 shapes are congruent.

Use your traced rhombus to find congruent shapes.
Write congruent or not congruent.

1.  flip → _____

2. 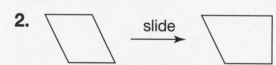 slide → _____

3. Which of these figures is congruent to  ? _____

    a. 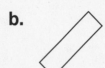   **b.**    **c.**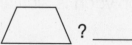

4. Which of these figures is not congruent to  ? _____

    a.   **b.**   **c.**

Exploring Line Symmetry

In your book you explored line symmetry by using grid paper. Here is another way to explore line symmetry.

A line of symmetry is a fold line when a figure is folded in half.

This figure has 1 line of symmetry. There is only one way to fold it exactly in half.

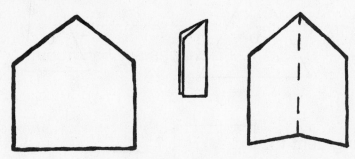

Look at the two halves of the figure. They match exactly.

Trace the figures below on to a piece of paper, then cut them out. Fold them in half in as many ways as possible. Draw their fold lines on the shapes below.

1.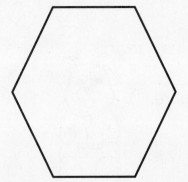

2.

3.

4.

Decision Making

1. Which polygon is similar to: 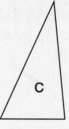 ? _____

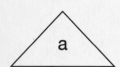 a

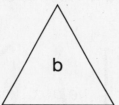 b

c

2. Which polygon is congruent to: ? _____

a

b

c

3. Use a protractor to draw a 60° angle in the space below.

4. Use a protractor to draw a 140° angle in the space below.

5. Is the figure to the right symmetrical? _____
   If so, draw a line of symmetry through the figure.

Name _____

Whole and Parts

Writing fractions to describe a part or parts of something
is easy when you follow these steps.

Step 1   Count the number of parts there are in all.

There are __4__ parts in the box. This number is
the **denominator**, the bottom number of a fraction. $\frac{?}{4}$

Step 2   Count the number of parts shaded.

There are __2__ shaded parts in the box. This
number is the **numerator**, the top number of a fraction. $\frac{2}{?}$

Step 3   The fraction that describes the
shaded parts of the entire box is: ___$\frac{2}{4}$___

Follow the steps to write fractions:
  a. to describe each shaded part.
  b. to describe each unshaded part.

1.   **a.** _____   **b.** _____

2.    **a.** _____   **b.** _____

3. 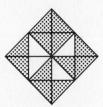   **a.** _____   **b.** _____

Exploring Equivalent Fractions

In your book, you explored equivalent fractions using fraction strips. Here is another way to work with equivalent fractions.

You can draw pictures to help you see if fractions are equivalent.

$\frac{3}{4}$ $\frac{2}{3}$ $\frac{6}{8}$

Step 1 Draw the same shape for each fraction. Choose a shape, like a rectangle, that is easy to divide into parts.

Step 2 Divide each shape into equal parts. Remember the denominator describes the total number of parts.

Step 3 Shade in the number of parts found in the numerator.

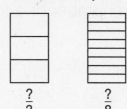

$\frac{?}{4}$ $\frac{?}{3}$ $\frac{?}{8}$

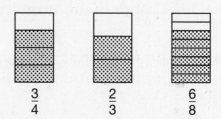

$\frac{3}{4}$ $\frac{2}{3}$ $\frac{6}{8}$

Step 4 Compare your pictures. For which fractions is the same area shaded?

The equivalent fractions are: ____$\frac{3}{4}$____ and ____$\frac{6}{8}$____.

Use the steps above to find pairs of equivalent fractions.

1. $\frac{4}{10}$ $\frac{2}{5}$ $\frac{1}{4}$

The equivalent fractions are _____ and _____.

2. $\frac{2}{3}$ $\frac{2}{8}$ $\frac{1}{4}$

The equivalent fractions are _____ and _____.

Name _____

Patterns with Equivalent Fractions

You can use pictures to help you identify equivalent fractions.

Find an equivalent fraction with a denominator of 12.

$\frac{2}{3}$

Draw a picture to represent the fraction.

Divide the shape into 12 equal parts.

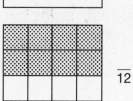

$\overline{12}$

Count the number of shaded squares. This is the numerator of the equivalent fraction.

$\frac{2}{3} = \frac{\boxed{8}}{12}$

Use the steps above to find equivalent fractions.

1. Find an equivalent fraction with a denominator of 10.

$\frac{3}{5} = \frac{\square}{10}$

2. Find an equivalent fraction with a denominator of 9.

$\frac{1}{3} = \frac{\square}{9}$

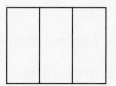

Find equivalent fractions with a denominator of 6.

3. $\frac{2}{3} = \frac{\square}{6}$ **4.** $\frac{1}{2} = \frac{\square}{6}$ **5.** $\frac{1}{3} = \frac{\square}{6}$

Find equivalent fractions with a denominator of 12.

6. $\frac{1}{6} = \frac{\square}{12}$ **7.** $\frac{1}{2} = \frac{\square}{12}$ **8.** $\frac{3}{4} = \frac{\square}{12}$

Name _____

Greatest Common Factor

You can use a table to find the greatest common factor of two numbers.

Find the greatest common factor of 12 and 16. Complete the tables for all possible factors of each number.

Circle all factors that appear in both charts. The greatest factor circled is the greatest common factor.

Factors of 12	
①	12
②	6
3	④

Factors of 16	
①	16
②	8
④	④

The greatest common factor of 12 and 16 is ___4___.

Use the steps above to find the greatest common factors of each pair of numbers.

1. The greatest common factor of 18 and 24 is _____.

Factors of 18	
	18
2	
	6

Factors of 24	
1	
	12
	8
4	

2. The greatest common factor of 21 and 28 is _____.

Factors of 21	
	21
3	

Factors of 28	
	28
2	14
4	

3. The greatest common factor of 25 and 30 is _____.

Factors of 25	
	25
5	

Factors of 30	
	30
2	15
3	10
5	

4. The greatest common factor of 16 and 20 is _____.

Factors of 16	
	16
2	8
4	

Factors of 20	
	20
2	10
4	

Simplest Form

Is $\frac{6}{12}$ in its simplest form?

Step 1 Ask: Is 1 the greatest common factor of the numerator and denominator?

$3 \times 2 = 6$ $6 \times 2 = 12$

2 is a common factor.

Step 2 Divide the numerator and denominator by the common factor, 2.

$$\frac{6}{12} = \frac{\overset{1}{\cancel{2}} \times 3}{\underset{1}{\cancel{2}} \times 6} = \frac{3}{6}$$

Step 3 Continue to look for common factors. Divide the numerator and denominator by the common factor. Continue until the only common factor is 1.

3 is a common factor.

$$\frac{3}{6} = \frac{\overset{1}{\cancel{3}} \times 1}{\underset{1}{\cancel{3}} \times 2} = \frac{1}{2}$$

The only factor in common to 1 and 2 is 1, so $\frac{1}{2}$ is in simplest form.

---

1. Circle fractions with 2 as a common factor.
Underline fractions with 3 as a common factor.

$\frac{2}{4}$ $\frac{6}{8}$ $\frac{3}{9}$ $\frac{4}{12}$ $\frac{2}{10}$

2. Circle fractions that are in simplest form.

$\frac{1}{8}$ $\frac{2}{6}$ $\frac{6}{9}$ $\frac{2}{3}$ $\frac{4}{5}$

Write each fraction in simplest form.

3. $\frac{12}{18}$ _____

4. $\frac{9}{12}$ _____

5. $\frac{16}{20}$ _____

6. $\frac{14}{18}$ _____

7. $\frac{6}{10}$ _____

8. $\frac{4}{16}$ _____

Name _____

Exploring Comparing and Ordering Fractions

In your book, you used fraction strips to compare and order fractions. Here are some rules to help you compare and order fractions.

Rule 1 If 2 fractions have a numerator of 1, the fraction with the lesser denominator is greater.

$\boxed{\frac{1}{2}}$ $\boxed{\frac{1}{3}}$ $\quad 2 < 3$

$\frac{1}{2} > \frac{1}{3}$

Rule 2 If 2 fractions have the same numerator, the fraction with the lesser denominator is greater.

$\boxed{\frac{2}{7}}$ $\boxed{\frac{2}{8}}$ $\quad 7 < 8$

$\frac{2}{7} > \frac{2}{8}$

Rule 3 If 2 fractions have the same denominator, the fraction with the greater numerator is greater.

$\boxed{\frac{3}{5}}$ $\boxed{\frac{2}{5}}$ $\quad 3 > 2$

$\frac{3}{5} > \frac{2}{5}$

Compare the fractions. Which fraction is greater?

1. $\frac{1}{4}$ $\frac{1}{8}$ 2. $\frac{3}{5}$ $\frac{3}{4}$ 3. $\frac{4}{9}$ $\frac{8}{9}$

_____   _____   _____

Compare the fractions. Write > or <. Use the three rules to help you.

4. $\frac{3}{10} \bigcirc \frac{3}{11}$ 5. $\frac{2}{5} \bigcirc \frac{3}{5}$ 6. $\frac{5}{6} \bigcirc \frac{5}{10}$

7. $\frac{4}{9} \bigcirc \frac{4}{6}$ 8. $\frac{7}{8} \bigcirc \frac{5}{8}$ 9. $\frac{1}{2} \bigcirc \frac{1}{4}$

Name _____

Comparing and Ordering Fractions

Compare $\frac{2}{3}$ and $\frac{3}{4}$.

How do you compare fractions like $\frac{2}{3}$ and $\frac{3}{4}$ that have different denominators and numerators?

Step 1 Find a common denominator by multiplying the denominators. A common denominator for $\frac{2}{3}$ and $\frac{3}{4}$ is 3×4 or 12.

Step 2 Change to equivalent fractions.

$\frac{2 \times 4}{3 \times 4} = \frac{8}{12}$
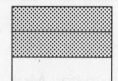   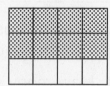

$\frac{2}{3}$ and $\frac{8}{12}$ are equivalent.

$\frac{3 \times 3}{4 \times 3} = \frac{9}{12}$
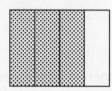   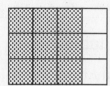

$\frac{3}{4}$ and $\frac{9}{12}$ are equivalent.

Step 3 You can see from the pictures that $\frac{9}{12} > \frac{8}{12}$.
So, $\frac{3}{4} > \frac{2}{3}$.

_____

Change to equivalent fractions. Then circle the greater fraction.

1. $\frac{1}{2} = \frac{}{10}$ $\frac{3}{5} = \frac{}{10}$ **2.** $\frac{5}{9} = \frac{}{18}$ $\frac{1}{3} = \frac{}{18}$

Compare. Write >, <, or = to complete. Use equivalent fractions.

3. $\frac{1}{4} \bigcirc \frac{3}{8}$ **4.** $\frac{2}{3} \bigcirc \frac{6}{9}$ **5.** $\frac{7}{8} \bigcirc \frac{7}{9}$

6. $\frac{1}{6} \bigcirc \frac{1}{8}$ **7.** $\frac{5}{9} \bigcirc \frac{1}{3}$ **8.** $\frac{8}{9} \bigcirc \frac{2}{3}$

Analyze Strategies: Make a Table

To solve some problems, it helps to put the data in a table.
Read the problem below.

Mr. Garcia, found a great sale on his favorite shirt. The sale
was two shirts for $15.00. He had $50 with him to purchase
the shirts. How many shirts could he purchase?

numbers of shirts	2	4	6	8
shirt price	$15	$30		

Look for a pattern. If 2 shirts cost $15, 4 shirts will cost
twice as much. So, 4 shirts will cost 2 × $15 = $30.

Complete the table. How many shirts can Mr. Garcia buy
for $50? __6__

Solve by making a table.

1. The Smith family had 3 left-handed family members for
   every 4 right-handed family members. As the family
   grows, how many left-handed family members will there
   be when there are 32 right-handed family members, if
   the pattern continues?

2. For every scoop of ice cream Sam sells, he sells 3 ice
   cream floats. How many floats did he sell when he sold
   8 scoops of ice cream?

Name _____

Exploring Mixed Numbers

In your book you used fraction strips to explore mixed numbers. Here is another way to see mixed numbers.

Make a drawing to show $3\frac{5}{8}$.

Draw 3 whole shapes to represent the whole number 3.

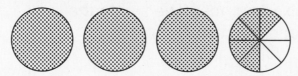

Draw one more whole shape. Divide it into the number of equal parts shown in the denominator. Shade the number of parts shown in the numerator.

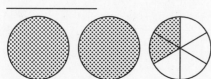

Match the pictures with the correct **mixed numbers** from the box.

| 4 | $2\frac{1}{4}$ | $1\frac{1}{3}$ | $3\frac{4}{6}$ | $2\frac{2}{6}$ | $1\frac{2}{5}$ |

1. _____

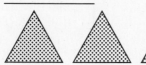

2. _____

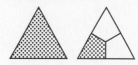

3. _____

4. _____

Write the mixed or whole number that names the shaded part.

5. _____

6. _____

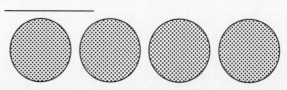

Mixed Numbers

You can use drawings to help you write mixed numbers and improper fractions.

Write $2\frac{1}{8}$ as an improper fraction.

Draw $2\frac{1}{8}$. Divide each whole into eighths.

 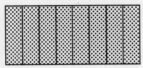 

Count the eighths. $2\frac{1}{8} = \frac{17}{8}$

Draw a picture for each mixed number. Then write the mixed number as an improper fraction.

1. $2\frac{1}{2} = \frac{\square}{2}$

2. $4\frac{3}{4} = \frac{\square}{4}$

3. $3\frac{2}{3} = \frac{\square}{3}$

4. $3\frac{3}{8} = \frac{\square}{8}$

Name _____

Exploring Comparing and Ordering Mixed Numbers

In your book you used fraction strips to compare and order mixed numbers. Here is another way to compare and order mixed numbers.

Example 1

Use a number line to compare $2\frac{5}{8}$ and $2\frac{3}{4}$. On a number line, $2\frac{5}{8}$ and $2\frac{3}{4}$ are between 2 and 3.

What is the common denominator of $\frac{5}{8}$ and $\frac{3}{4}$? __8__

Divide the space on the number line into 8 parts.

Mark $2\frac{5}{8}$ and $2\frac{3}{4}$ on the number line.

Because $2\frac{3}{4}$ is closer to 3, $2\frac{3}{4}$ is greater than $2\frac{5}{8}$. $2\frac{3}{4} > 2\frac{5}{8}$

Example 2

Use a number line to put $1\frac{3}{4}$, $1\frac{2}{3}$, and $1\frac{5}{6}$ in order from least to greatest.

All three numbers are between which two whole numbers? __1 and 2__

What is the common denominator? __12__

Show the three numbers on the number line.

List the three numbers in order from least to greatest. $1\frac{2}{3}$; $1\frac{3}{4}$; $1\frac{5}{6}$

Compare. Use > or <.

1. $2\frac{1}{2}$ and $1\frac{3}{4}$ _____

2. $3\frac{1}{3}$ and $3\frac{1}{2}$ _____

3. $1\frac{3}{4}$ and $1\frac{7}{8}$ _____

4. $\frac{3}{2}$ and $\frac{11}{6}$ _____

Write in order from least to greatest.

5. $2\frac{3}{4}$, $2\frac{1}{6}$, $2\frac{1}{2}$ _____

6. $\frac{13}{3}$, $\frac{9}{2}$, $\frac{12}{5}$ _____

Understanding Percent

The word "per cent" means "out of one hundred."

For example $\frac{30}{100}$ is 30 out of 100, or 30%.

How many squares
are there in the drawing? __100__

How many squares are shaded? __30__

The shaded part can be described as:

30 out of 100 $\frac{30}{100}$ 30%

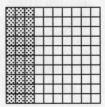

---

1. a. How many squares are

   in the drawing? _____

   b. How many squares are shaded? _____

   c. The shaded part can be

   described as _____ out of _____.

   d. Describe the shaded part with a fraction. _____

   e. Describe the shaded part with a percent. _____

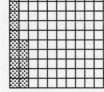

Write the percent shaded in each drawing.

2. _____

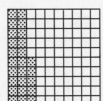

3. _____

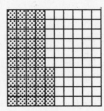

Rewrite the fractions as a percent.

4. $\frac{35}{100}$ _____

5. $\frac{42}{100}$ _____

6. $\frac{63}{100}$ _____

7. $\frac{58}{100}$ _____

8. $\frac{77}{100}$ _____

9. $\frac{21}{100}$ _____

Connecting Fractions, Decimals, and Percents

There are 100 rides on the bus pass, and 25 of them have been used.

Write a fraction, a decimal, and a percent to tell how many rides have been used.

Bus Pass

Fraction: $\frac{25}{100}$

Decimal: 0.25   Use a decimal point to show hundredths.

Percent: 25%   Use a percent sign to mean "out of 100."

Write a fraction, a decimal and a percent to tell how many rides are left on the bus pass.

Fraction: $\frac{75}{100}$

Decimal: 0.75   Use a decimal point to show hundredths.

Percent: 75%   Use a percent sign to mean "out of 100."

Write a fraction, a decimal, and a percent that name each shaded part and unshaded part.

1. shaded part _____

   unshaded part _____

2. shaded part _____

   unshaded part _____

3. shaded part _____

   unshaded part _____

4. shaded part _____

   unshaded part _____

Decision Making

The table shows the results of a survey Mr. Andrews took of the students in his class.

Which Kind of Story Do You Like Best?	
Stories about animals	|||| ||||
Stories about people	|||| |||| ||||

Count the total number of tally marks.
How many students were surveyed? __25__

Ten of the students liked stories about animals best, so $\frac{10}{25}$ of the students chose stories about animals.

To write $\frac{10}{25}$ as a percent, multiply numerator and denominator by 4, because $25 \times 4 = 100$; $\frac{10}{25} = \frac{40}{100}$.
Of the 25 students, 40% chose stories about animals.

You can find the number of students who chose stories about people by subtracting 40% from 100%. Of the 25 students, 60% chose stories about people.

1. Make a survey of 10 students in your class. Ask them which kind of stories they like best, stories about animals or stories about people.

   a. How can you write the results of your survey as percents?

   b. How do your results compare with the results in Mr. Andrews' class?

2. Compare your results in Exercise 1 with the results of other students in your class. Are your results similar or are they different?

Name _____

Adding and Subtracting Fractions with Like Denominators

Drawing pictures can help you add and subtract fractions with like denominators.

$\frac{7}{8} + \frac{5}{8}$

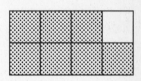

Step 1 Look at the denominator. Draw a shape divided into the number of parts in the denominator.

Step 2 Shade in the number of parts described by the first fraction.

Step 3 a. To add, shade in the second fraction. Draw another shape if you run out of sections to shade. Then count the number of shaded pieces in all. Remember to count a fully shaded piece as one whole.

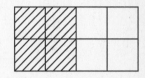

$$\frac{7}{8} + \frac{5}{8} = 1\frac{4}{8} = 1\frac{1}{2}$$

$\frac{5}{8} - \frac{2}{8}$

b. To subtract, shade the second fraction over the first fraction. Then count the number of pieces shaded once.

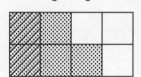

$$\frac{5}{8} - \frac{2}{8} = \frac{3}{8}$$

Divide each rectangle into equal parts and use shading to help you find each sum or difference. Simplify.

1. $\frac{3}{9} + \frac{3}{9} =$ _____

2. $\frac{7}{9} - \frac{4}{9} =$ _____

3. $\frac{7}{10} + \frac{3}{10} =$ _____

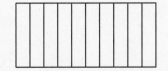

4. $\frac{8}{10} - \frac{2}{10} =$ _____

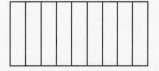

Exploring Adding Fractions

In your book, you explored sums using fraction strips.
Here is another way to add fractions with unlike denominators.

$\frac{3}{4} + \frac{3}{8}$

You can use a ruler to help you find the sum.

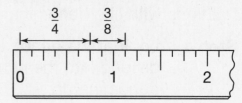

$\frac{3}{4} = \frac{6}{8}$

$\frac{6}{8} + \frac{3}{8} = \frac{9}{8} = 1\frac{1}{8}$

Use the ruler provided to help you find each sum.

1. $\frac{1}{4} + \frac{1}{2} =$ _____

2. $\frac{5}{8} + \frac{1}{4} =$ _____

3. $\frac{3}{4} + \frac{1}{8} =$ _____

4. $\frac{1}{4} + \frac{1}{8} =$ _____

5. $\frac{7}{8} + \frac{3}{4} =$ _____

6. $\frac{1}{2} + \frac{5}{8} =$ _____

Least Common Denominator

Find the least common denominator (LCD) for $\frac{1}{3}$ and $\frac{3}{4}$.

The denominator of $\frac{1}{3}$ is 3. The denominator of $\frac{3}{4}$ is 4.

What is the least number that is a multiple of both 3 and 4?
This number is the least common denominator.

Find some multiples of 3:	Find some multiples of 4:
$3 \times 1 = 3$	$4 \times 1 = 4$
$3 \times 2 = 6$	$4 \times 2 = 8$
$3 \times 3 = \underline{\ 9\ }$	$4 \times 3 = \underline{\ 12\ }$
$3 \times 4 = \underline{\ 12\ }$	$4 \times 4 = \underline{\ 16\ }$
$3 \times 5 = \underline{\ 15\ }$	$4 \times 5 = \underline{\ 20\ }$
$3 \times 6 = \underline{\ 18\ }$	$4 \times 6 = \underline{\ 24\ }$
$3 \times 7 = \underline{\ 21\ }$	
$3 \times 8 = \underline{\ 24\ }$	

Some multiples of 3 are:

3, 6, 9, 12, 15, 18, 21, 24.

Some multiples of 4 are:

4, 8, 12, 16, 20, 24.

Which numbers above are multiples of both 3 and 4? __12 and 24__

Which of the two multiples is the lesser number? __12__

So, the least common denominator of $\frac{1}{3}$ and $\frac{3}{4}$

Find the least common denominator (LCD) for each pair of fractions.

1. $\frac{3}{5}$ and $\frac{1}{4}$

    a. List some multiples of 5. Start with the least numbers.

    _____

    b. List some multiples of 4. Start with the least numbers.

    _____

    c. Which numbers above are multiples of both 5 and 4? _____

    d. What is the LCD for $\frac{3}{5}$ and $\frac{1}{4}$? _____

2. $\frac{5}{6}$ and $\frac{3}{7}$ _____   **3.** $\frac{1}{5}$ and $\frac{2}{3}$ _____   **4.** $\frac{1}{8}$ and $\frac{1}{6}$ _____

Adding Fractions

Find $\frac{3}{4} + \frac{1}{6}$.

One number that you can always use as a common denominator is the product of the denominators.

Find the equivalent fractions by multiplying each fraction by the other fraction's denominator.

$$\frac{3 \times 6}{4 \times 6} = \frac{18}{24}$$

$$\frac{1 \times 4}{6 \times 4} = \frac{4}{24}$$

Add the equivalent fractions.

$$\begin{array}{r} \frac{18}{24} \\ + \frac{4}{24} \\ \hline \frac{22}{24} \end{array}$$

Simplify by dividing by a common factor.

$$\frac{22 \div 2}{24 \div 2} = \frac{11}{12}$$

Follow the same steps to find each sum.

1. Add $\frac{2}{3}$ and $\frac{1}{4}$.

a. Write the equivalent fractions.

$$\frac{2 \times 4}{3 \times 4} = \frac{\Box}{\Box}$$

$$\frac{1 \times \Box}{4 \times \Box} = \frac{\Box}{\Box}$$

b. Add the equivalent fractions.

$$\begin{array}{r} \frac{\Box}{12} \\ + \frac{\Box}{12} \\ \hline \frac{\Box}{12} \end{array}$$

2. $\begin{array}{r} \frac{1}{5} \\ + \frac{5}{6} \\ \hline \end{array}$

3. $\begin{array}{r} \frac{3}{4} \\ + \frac{5}{8} \\ \hline \end{array}$

4. $\begin{array}{r} \frac{1}{8} \\ + \frac{1}{3} \\ \hline \end{array}$

5. $\begin{array}{r} \frac{8}{9} \\ + \frac{1}{6} \\ \hline \end{array}$

Name _____

Exploring Subtracting Fractions

In your book, you explored differences using fraction strips.
Here is another way to subtract fractions with unlike denominators.

$\frac{3}{8} - \frac{1}{4}$

You can find the LCD (8) and draw pictures to help you find the difference.

Find equivalent fractions by using the LCD. Draw
a shape divided into the same number of equal parts
as the LCD.

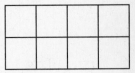

Shade in the number of parts found $\frac{3}{8} = \frac{3}{8}$ $\frac{1}{4} = \frac{2}{8}$
in the greater numerator. (3) Cross off
the number of parts found in the
lesser numerator. (2)

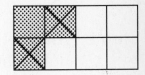

Count the number of pieces shaded but not crossed out (1).

$\frac{3}{8} - \frac{1}{4} = \frac{1}{8}$

Use the shapes provided to help you find each difference.

1. $\frac{1}{2} - \frac{1}{4} =$ _____

2. $\frac{5}{6} - \frac{2}{3} =$ _____

3. $\frac{7}{8} - \frac{3}{4} =$ _____

4. $\frac{2}{3} - \frac{1}{2} =$ _____

Name _____

Subtracting Fractions

You can use drawings to help you subtract fractions.

Find the difference of $\frac{4}{5}$ and $\frac{1}{2}$. $\frac{4}{5} - \frac{1}{2}$

Step 1   Find the LCM, or least common multiple, of 5 and 2.

2	4	6	8	⑩	12
5	⑩	15	20	25	30

The LCM of 5 and 2 is 10.

Draw 2 rectangles and divide them into 10 equal parts.

Step 2   Divide the first rectangle
into 5ths.

Divide the second rectangle
in half.

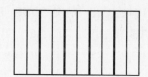 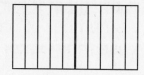

Step 3   Shade $\frac{4}{5}$ of the first rectangle
and $\frac{1}{2}$ of the second. Notice
that the shaded parts are
the same size Write the
equivalent fractions.

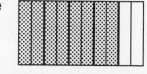 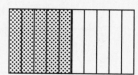

$\frac{4}{5} = \frac{8}{10}$ $\frac{1}{2} = \frac{5}{10}$

Step 4

Subtract the numerators and simplify if possible.

$\frac{8}{10} - \frac{5}{10} = \frac{3}{10}$

Find the difference. Simplify. Use drawings to help you.

1. $\frac{3}{4} = \frac{9}{12}$

$\frac{1}{3} = \frac{\square}{12}$

2. $\frac{2}{3} = \frac{\square}{6}$

$\frac{1}{2} = \frac{\square}{6}$

3. $\frac{3}{5} - \frac{5}{10} =$ _____

4. $\frac{1}{2} - \frac{3}{8} =$ _____

Name _____

Analyze Word Problems: Too Much or Too Little Information

The swim team practices for $\frac{1}{3}$ hr between 2 P.M. and 3 P.M. The track team runs for less than an hour between 2 and 3 P.M. How much longer do the swimmers practice than the runners?

Ask yourself:

What do I know?

The swim team practices ___$\frac{1}{3}$___ hour.

The track team runs __don't know__ hours.

What do I need to find out?

__How much longer the swim team practices than the track team__

Can I find the information I need?

__No, the part of the hour the track team runs is not given.__

Write if each problem has too much or too little information. Solve if possible. Tell what is needed if you can't solve.

1. One box weighed $\frac{7}{8}$ lb. The box next to it weighed more than 1 lb. Find the difference in their weights.

_____

_____

2. The cook at the diner scrambled $\frac{1}{2}$ of the eggs served. One-fourth of the eggs were fried, and $\frac{1}{8}$ were boiled. How many eggs are left?

_____

_____

3. The park has 10 swings, of which $\frac{2}{5}$ are broken. Half the swings have metal seats and $\frac{1}{10}$ of the swings have wooden seats. How many more swings have metal seats than wooden seats?

_____

Name _____

Exploring Adding and Subtracting Mixed Numbers

In your book you added and subtracted mixed numbers using fraction strips. Here is another way to find sums and differences of mixed numbers.

Example 1 $2\frac{3}{4} - 1\frac{1}{4}$

Draw a picture to show $2\frac{3}{4}$.

Draw an X through one of the small squares to subtract $\frac{1}{4}$.

Draw an X through one of the large squares to subtract 1.

Example 2 $2\frac{1}{2} - \frac{1}{4}$

Draw a picture to show $2\frac{1}{2}$.

So you can subtract $\frac{1}{4}$, divide the square on the right into fourths.

Draw an X through one of the small squares to subtract $\frac{1}{4}$.

Write the fraction that describes the shaded portion remaining.

$2\frac{3}{4} - 1\frac{1}{4} = \underline{\quad 1\frac{1}{2} \quad}$

$2\frac{1}{2} - \frac{1}{4} = \underline{\quad 2\frac{1}{4} \quad}$

Add or subtract the mixed numbers. Draw pictures to help. Simplify.

1. $1\frac{1}{4}$
   $+\ 3\frac{1}{4}$

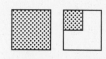

2. $3\frac{3}{4}$
   $-\ 2\frac{1}{4}$

3. $2\frac{1}{2}$
   $+\ 1\frac{1}{2}$

4. $2\frac{1}{4}$
   $+\ 4\frac{1}{2}$

5. $1\frac{1}{2}$
   $-\ \frac{1}{4}$

Name _____

Estimating Sums and Differences

Round to estimate the sum.

$1\frac{3}{4} + 2\frac{1}{4}$

$\frac{3}{4}$ is greater than $\frac{1}{2}$, so $\frac{3}{4}$
rounds to 1.

$\frac{1}{4}$ is less than $\frac{1}{2}$, so $\frac{1}{4}$
rounds to 0.

$1\frac{3}{4}$ is about 2.

$2\frac{1}{4}$ is about 2.

$1\frac{3}{4} + 2\frac{1}{4}$

Add the two numbers to estimate the answer. $2 + 2 = 4$

_____

Estimate each sum or difference. Round each
mixed number.

1. $7\frac{1}{2} + 6\frac{1}{4}$ $\frac{1}{2}$ rounds to __1__

$\frac{1}{4}$ rounds to __0__

So, $7\frac{1}{2} + 6\frac{1}{4}$ is about _____ + _____ = _____

2. $5\frac{2}{3} - 2\frac{1}{3}$ $\frac{2}{3}$ rounds to _____

$\frac{1}{3}$ rounds to _____

So, $5\frac{2}{3} - 2\frac{1}{3}$ is about _____ - _____ = _____

3. $8\frac{1}{4} + 2\frac{3}{4} =$ _____   **4.** $5\frac{1}{2} + 2\frac{2}{5} =$ _____

5. $9\frac{5}{8} - 1\frac{3}{4} =$ _____   **6.** $8\frac{1}{4} - 6\frac{1}{3} =$ _____

7. $8\frac{5}{6} - 4\frac{2}{3} =$ _____   **8.** $7\frac{1}{5} + 1\frac{2}{3} =$ _____

9. $6\frac{3}{8} - 4\frac{7}{8} =$ _____   **10.** $3\frac{4}{5} + 9\frac{1}{3} =$ _____

11. $9\frac{1}{6} - 1\frac{2}{5} =$ _____   **12.** $6\frac{1}{3} - 5\frac{7}{8} =$ _____

Adding and Subtracting
Mixed Numbers

You can use drawings to help you add and subtract mixed numbers.

$3\frac{3}{4}$

$+\ 5\frac{1}{3}$

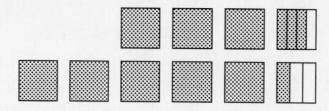

Find the LCM of 4 and 3.

The LCM is 12.

Divide each of the fraction drawings into 12 pieces.

Use your drawings to write equivalent fractions.

Then add.

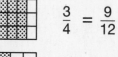

$\frac{3}{4} = \frac{9}{12}$

$\frac{1}{3} = \frac{4}{12}$

$3\frac{3}{4}\ =\ \ \ \ 3\frac{9}{12}$

$+\ 5\frac{1}{3}\ =\ +\ 5\frac{4}{12}$

$\qquad\qquad 8\frac{13}{12} = 8 + 1\frac{1}{12} = 9\frac{1}{12}$

$3\frac{3}{4} + 5\frac{1}{3} = 9\frac{1}{12}$

Find the sums or differences. Draw pictures to help.

1. $\qquad 6\frac{3}{5}\ =\ \ 6\frac{\square}{10}$

$\qquad -\ 4\frac{3}{10}\ =\ -\ 4\frac{\square}{10}$

$\qquad\qquad\qquad\quad 2\frac{\square}{10}$

2. $\qquad 3\frac{2}{3}\ =\ \ 3\frac{\square}{\square}$

$\qquad +\ 4\frac{3}{4}\ =\ +\ 4\frac{\square}{\square}$

3. $\qquad 5\frac{4}{5}$

$\qquad -\ 1\frac{1}{2}$

4. $\qquad 4\frac{1}{2}$

$\qquad +\ 2\frac{3}{4}$

5. $\qquad 2\frac{1}{2}$

$\qquad -\ 1\frac{2}{5}$

Adding Mixed Numbers

Find $2\frac{1}{4} + 1\frac{1}{2} + 4\frac{5}{6}$.

First you must change the fractions
so they all have the same denominator.

$$2\frac{1}{4}$$
$$1\frac{1}{2}$$
$$+\ 4\frac{5}{6}$$

Find the number that is divisible by all three denominators.
This number is the least common denominator (LCD).

The denominators are 4, 2, and 6. What is the least number
divisible by 4, 2, and 6? 12 is divisible by 4, 2, and 6.
12 is the **least common denominator**.

Write each fraction as an equivalent fraction with the least
common denominator.

$\frac{1}{4} = \frac{?}{12}$ $12 \div 4 = 3,\ 3 \times 1 = 3,$ so $\frac{1}{4} = \frac{3}{12}$

$\frac{1}{2} = \frac{?}{12}$ $12 \div 2 = 6,\ 6 \times 1 = 6,$ so $\frac{1}{2} = \frac{6}{12}$

$\frac{5}{6} = \frac{?}{12}$ $12 \div 6 = 2,\ 2 \times 5 = 10,$ so $\frac{5}{6} = \frac{10}{12}$

$$2\frac{3}{12}$$
$$1\frac{6}{12}$$
$$+\ 4\frac{10}{12} \qquad \text{Simplify}$$
$$7\frac{19}{12} \qquad \frac{19}{12} = 1\frac{7}{12} \qquad 7 + 1\frac{7}{12} = \underline{8\frac{7}{12}}$$

$2\frac{1}{4} + 1\frac{1}{2} + 4\frac{5}{6} = \underline{8\frac{7}{12}}$

---

1. $3\frac{2}{3} + 2\frac{1}{2} + 2\frac{1}{4}$

   a. What is the smallest number divisible by 3, 2, and 4? _____

   b. Write each fraction as an equivalent fraction with the

      least common denominator. _____

   c. Now add the fractions. What is the sum of the fractions? _____

   d. Simplify the sum. _____   **e.** $3\frac{2}{3} + 2\frac{1}{2} + 2\frac{1}{4} =$ _____

2. $1\frac{1}{8} + 2\frac{3}{4} + 3\frac{1}{2} =$ _____   **3.** $6\frac{5}{6} + 4\frac{1}{8} + 5\frac{2}{3} =$ _____

Subtracting Mixed Numbers

Example 1 Find $3\frac{1}{8} - 1\frac{1}{2}$.

First, change the fractions so they all have the
same denominator.

Find a number that is divisible by both denominators.
This number is the common denominator.

The denominators are 8 and 2. 8 is divisible by 8 and 2,
so 8 is the common denominator.

Write each fraction as an equivalent fraction with the
least common denominator.

$$\frac{1}{8} = \frac{1}{8} \qquad \frac{1}{2} = \frac{?}{8} \qquad \frac{1 \times 4}{2 \times 4} = \frac{4}{8} \qquad \begin{array}{r} 3\frac{1}{8} \\ - 1\frac{4}{8} \\ \hline \end{array}$$

Since you can not take away $\frac{4}{8}$ from $\frac{1}{8}$, regroup.

$$1 = \frac{8}{8} \qquad \frac{8}{8} + \frac{1}{8} = \frac{9}{8} \qquad 3\frac{1}{8} \rightarrow \begin{array}{r} 2\frac{9}{8} \\ - 1\frac{1}{2} \rightarrow - 1\frac{4}{8} \\ \hline 1\frac{5}{8} \end{array} \quad \text{So, } 3\frac{1}{8} - 1\frac{1}{2} = 1\frac{5}{8}.$$

Example 2 Find $4 - 2\frac{3}{4}$.

Since there is no fraction from which to subtract $\frac{3}{4}$, regroup.

$$\begin{array}{r} 4 \\ - 2\frac{3}{4} \\ \hline \end{array} \qquad 1 = \frac{4}{4} \longrightarrow \begin{array}{r} 3\frac{4}{4} \\ \longrightarrow - 2\frac{3}{4} \\ \hline 1\frac{1}{4} \end{array} \quad \text{So, } 4 - 2\frac{3}{4} = 1\frac{1}{4}.$$

---

1. $6\frac{1}{3} - 2\frac{4}{9}$

   a. What number is divisible by 3 and 9? _____

   b. Subtract the fractions. Did you need to regroup? _____

   c. $6\frac{1}{3} - 2\frac{4}{9} =$ _____

2. $7 - 2\frac{2}{5} =$ _____   **3.** $4\frac{4}{5} - 2\frac{1}{2} =$ _____   **4.** $5 - 1\frac{1}{2} =$ _____

Compare Strategies:
Work Backward/Draw a Picture

The scouts worked at a car wash to raise money. They raised twice
as much money on Saturday as they did on Friday. On Sunday, they
earned three times what they earned on Saturday. On Friday, they had
earned $86. What did they earn on Saturday? on Sunday?

You know that the scouts earned $86 on Friday. You can draw a
picture and work backward to find out how much they earned on
Saturday and Sunday.

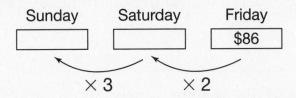

Find the amount earned on Saturday. 2 × $86 = $172, so they earned
$172 on Saturday. Write $172 in the box for Saturday above.

Find the amount earned on Sunday. 3 × $172 = $516, so they earned
$516 on Sunday. Write $516 in the box for Sunday above.

The scouts earned $172 on Saturday and $516 on Sunday.

Work backward from an answer to solve the problem.

1. Lin rode his bike to the store. He rode twice as long on Cherry
Lane as he did on 1st St. He rode 0.2 mi more on 1st St. than on
Jay Rd. Lin rode his bike 0.8 mi on Jay Rd. How far did Lin ride his
bike to the store?

a. Draw boxes and arrows to show how you will work backward.

b. How far did Lin ride his bike on each street?

_____

c. How far did Lin ride to the store? _____

Name _____

Linear Measure

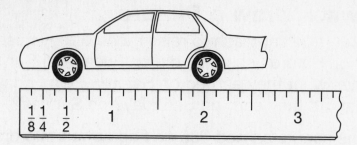

Measure the model car to the nearest $\frac{1}{2}$-inch. It is between $2\frac{1}{2}$ and 3 in. long. It is closer to $2\frac{1}{2}$ than 3 in., so the car measures $2\frac{1}{2}$ in. to the nearest $\frac{1}{2}$-inch.

---

1. Measure the car to the nearest $\frac{1}{4}$-inch.

    a. The car is between $2\frac{1}{2}$ and _____ in. long.

    b. The car measures _____ in. to the nearest $\frac{1}{4}$-inch.

2. Measure the car to the nearest $\frac{1}{8}$-inch.

    a. The car is between _____ and _____ in. long.

    b. The car measures _____ in. to the nearest $\frac{1}{8}$-inch.

Find the length to the nearest $\frac{1}{4}$-inch.

3. _____

Find the length to the nearest $\frac{1}{8}$-inch.

4. _____

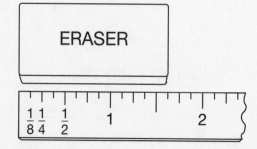

Name _____

Feet, Yards, and Miles

Example 1   27 inches = _____ feet _____ inches

Use cubes to help you find the answer.

12 inches = 1 foot. If each cube in 1 inch long,
12 cubes = 1 foot.

Line up 27 cubes in groups of 12 cubes to show feet.

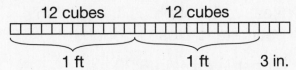

How many groups of 12 do you have? __2__

How many cubes are left over? __3__

So, 27 inches = 2 feet 3 inches

Example 2   2 yards 2 feet = _____ feet

Use addition to help you find the answer. 1 yard = 3 feet

$$
\begin{array}{l}
1 \text{ yard} \longrightarrow 3 \text{ feet} \\
1 \text{ yard} \longrightarrow 3 \text{ feet} \\
\underline{+\ 2\ \text{feet}} \longrightarrow \underline{2\ \text{feet}} \\
8 \text{ feet}
\end{array}
\qquad \text{So, 2 yards 2 feet = 8 feet}
$$

_____

1. 22 feet = _____ yd _____ ft

    a. Use cubes. If each cube represents
1 foot, how many cubes would equal 1 yard? _____

    b. Draw cubes in the space below to show yards and feet.

    c. 22 feet = _____ yd _____ ft

2. 4 feet 4 inches = _____ in.

    a. Use addition. Write the number sentence you would use.

_____

    b. 4 feet 4 inches = _____ in.

3. 31 in. = _____ ft _____ in.   **4.** 5 yd 1 ft = _____ ft

Analyze Word Problems:
Exact or Estimate?

Derek walks his dog for 30 minutes every evening after
doing dishes. Derek's family has dinner at about 6:30 P.M.
The family usually finishes eating in about 40 minutes.
The dishes usually ake about 15 minutes. About what time
does Derek walk the dog?

Hint: When a problem uses words such as "about," this
usually means an estimate is close enough.

What do you know?   Dinner is around 6:30 P.M.

Eating takes about 40 min.

Dishes take about 15 min.

40 min and 15 min is about 1 hour.

Derek walks his dog at about 7:30 P.M.

Decide whether you need an estimate or exact answer. Solve.

1. Laura needs to read 30 more pages for homework,
which will take about 20 minutes, after dinner. She
wants to do this before walking the dog. Laura
finished eating at 5:30. About what time will she be
able to walk the dog?

_____

2. Your mom sent you to the grocery store to buy some
bread and milk, which cost $3.45. You give the clerk a
$5.00 bill. How much change should you receive?

_____

3. You earn $10 each day you help at the animal clinic. You
want to buy 2 CD's that cost $19.95 each. How many
days will you have to work to earn the money for the
CD's?

_____

Name _____

Exploring Multiplication of Whole Numbers by Fractions

In your book you multiplied whole numbers by fractions using counters. Here is another way to multiply by fractions.

Find $\frac{1}{3}$ of 9.

Draw 9 squares. Divide them into 3 equal groups. One of the groups shows $\frac{1}{3}$ of 9. There are ___3___ squares in each group, so $\frac{1}{3}$ of 9 is ___3___.

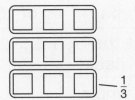

Find $\frac{2}{5}$ of 10.

Draw 10 squares. Divide them into 5 equal groups. One of the groups shows $\frac{1}{5}$ of 10, so 2 groups show $\frac{2}{5}$ of 10. There are ___2___ squares in each group, so $\frac{2}{5}$ of 10 = 2 × 2 = ___4___.

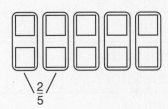

---

1. Find $\frac{1}{4}$ of 8

  a. Draw 8 squares.

  b. Divide the squares into 4 equal groups.

  c. How many squares are in each group? _____

  d. $\frac{1}{4}$ of 8 is _____

2. Find $\frac{2}{3}$ of 9

  a. Draw 9 squares.

  b. Divide the squares into 3 equal groups.

  c. How many squares are in each group? _____

  d. $\frac{2}{3}$ of 9 is _____

3. $\frac{1}{6}$ of 12 is _____

4. $\frac{3}{5}$ of 15 is _____

5. $\frac{3}{8}$ of 16 is _____

6. $\frac{1}{9}$ of 27 is _____

Multiplying with Fractions

You can use the numerator and denominator of fractions to help you multiply a whole number by a fraction. This table gives an example. Fill in the missing information to see how the table works.

Steps	$\frac{1}{5}$ of 15	$\frac{2}{5}$ of 15	$\frac{3}{5}$ of 15	$\frac{4}{5}$ of 15
What is the denominator?	5	5	5	5
Divide whole number by the denominator.	15 ÷ 5	15 ÷ 5	15 ÷ 5	15 ÷ 5
Quotient	3	3	3	3
What is the numerator?	1	2	3	4
Multiply numerator by the answer above.	1 × 3	2 × 3	3 × 3	4 × 3
Product	3	6	9	12

Find each product. Follow the steps above. Use mental math.

1. $\frac{1}{5}$ of 20 _____

2. $\frac{1}{4}$ of 24 _____

3. $\frac{1}{3}$ of 18 _____

4. $\frac{1}{10}$ of 30 _____

5. $\frac{1}{6}$ of 12 _____

6. $\frac{3}{5}$ of 10 _____

7. $\frac{2}{5}$ of 20 _____

8. $\frac{3}{4}$ of 24 _____

9. $\frac{2}{3}$ of 18 _____

10. $\frac{1}{7}$ of 28 _____

11. $\frac{1}{9}$ of 27 _____

12. $\frac{3}{8}$ of 32 _____

Estimating Products

Fill in the chart below to see how different methods of estimating products of fractions work.

METHOD	EXAMPLES	THINK
Round to the nearest whole number.	$1\frac{4}{5} \times 7$ $3\frac{7}{8} \times 8$	• $1\frac{4}{5}$ is near 2 • $2 \times 7 = 14$ • estimate: 14 • $3\frac{7}{8}$ is near $\underline{4}$ • $\underline{4} \times 8 = \underline{32}$ • estimate: $\underline{32}$
Use compatible numbers (numbers that divide evenly).	$\frac{1}{4} \times 25$ $\frac{2}{7} \times 48$	• 4 goes evenly into 24. • $\frac{1}{4} \times 24 = 6$ • estimate: 6 • 7 goes evenly into $\underline{49}$ • $\frac{2}{7} \times \underline{49} = (\underline{49} \div 7) \times 2 = \underline{14}$ • estimate: $\underline{14}$
Replace the fraction with a benchmark.	$\frac{3}{8} \times 20$ $\frac{4}{9} \times 20$	• $\frac{3}{8}$ is near $\frac{4}{8}$, or $\frac{1}{2}$. • $\frac{1}{2} \times 20 = 10$ • estimate: 10 • $\frac{4}{9}$ is near $\underline{\frac{1}{2}}$ • $\frac{1}{2} \times 20 = \underline{10}$ • estimate: $\underline{10}$

Estimate each product.

1. $\frac{1}{5} \times 31$ _____

2. $\frac{7}{9} \times 10$ _____

3. $\frac{1}{6} \times 43$ _____

4. $\frac{6}{11} \times 20$ _____

Exploring Multiplication of Fractions by Fractions

In your book, you found fractions of fractions by folding paper. Here is another way to multiply fractions by fractions.

Step 1 To find $\frac{1}{2}$ of $\frac{1}{3}$, start with a rectangle.

Step 2 Divide the rectangle into 3 parts. Each part is $\frac{1}{3}$. Lightly shade $\frac{1}{3}$.

Step 3 Divide the rectangle in half horizontally. Shade $\frac{1}{2}$ of the rectangle. Now there are 6 parts. Each part is $\frac{1}{6}$.

Step 4 Count the sections that were shaded twice. One out of the 6 sections was shaded twice. So, $\frac{1}{2}$ of $\frac{1}{3}$ is $\underline{\ \frac{1}{6}\ }$.

Use the drawing to help you find $\frac{1}{4}$ of $\frac{1}{2}$.

1. Divide the rectangle into 2 parts.

   Shade 1 part.

   Each part is _____.

2. Divide the rectangle into fourths.

   Shade $\frac{1}{4}$.

   Each part is _____.

   $\frac{1}{4}$ of $\frac{1}{2}$ is _____.

Name _____

Multiplying Fractions

Common factors can help you multiply fractions by fractions.

Think about these fractions. Can you simplify them?

$\frac{4}{10}$ $\frac{2}{8}$

- To simplify fractions, factor each numerator and denominator.

$\frac{4}{10} = \frac{2 \times 2}{2 \times 5}$ $\frac{2}{8} = \frac{2 \times 1}{2 \times 4}$

- Then divide by common factors.

$\frac{4}{10} = \frac{\cancel{2} \times 2}{\cancel{2} \times 5} = \frac{2}{5}$ $\frac{2}{8} = \frac{\cancel{2} \times 1}{\cancel{2} \times 4} = \frac{1}{4}$

When you multiply fractions, you can use the same method of dividing common factors.

Find $\frac{1}{4} \times \frac{4}{5}$. The common factor is 4.

$\frac{1}{4} \times \frac{4}{5} = \frac{\cancel{4} \times 1}{\cancel{4} \times 5} = \frac{1}{5}$

Simplify the fractions.

1. $\frac{6}{8} = \frac{2 \times 3}{2 \times 4} =$ _____

2. $\frac{5}{10} = \frac{5 \times 1}{5 \times 2} =$ _____

Find the product. Simplify.

3. $\frac{3}{8} \times \frac{1}{3} = \frac{3 \times 1}{3 \times 8} =$ _____

4. $\frac{1}{2} \times \frac{4}{5} = \frac{4 \times 1}{2 \times 5} = \frac{4}{10} =$ _____

5. $\frac{2}{10} \times \frac{3}{5} =$ _____

6. $\frac{6}{8} \times \frac{2}{10} =$ _____

7. $\frac{4}{4} \times \frac{5}{16} =$ _____

8. $\frac{2}{6} \times \frac{6}{12} =$ _____

9. $\frac{5}{10} \times \frac{3}{5} =$ _____

10. $\frac{2}{3} \times \frac{3}{11} =$ _____

Analyze Word Problems:
Overestimating and Underestimating

Terence has $4.45 in his pocket, $7.93 at home, and $2.19 in his desk. Can he buy a $10.95 book with the total amount of money?

Terence wants to be sure he has enough money. If he rounds each amount to higher dollar amounts, his estimate will be greater than the actual amount he has.

Terence should underestimate.

   Round each amount to a lesser dollar amount.

      $4.45 is close to $4.00

      $7.95 is close to $7.00

      $2.19 is close to __$2.00__.

   Add the three rounded dollar amounts.

      __$4.00__ + __$7.00__ + __$2.00__ = __$13.00__

Since all the dollar amounts were lowered, Terence has at least $13.00. So, he can buy a book for $10.95

Karol must earn 500 points in order to receive an A in math class. She has earned the following points so far—85, 92, 79, 99, and 87. She has one more project. If she earns 50 points, will she receive an A?

1. Should you overestimate or underestimate to solve the problem? Why?

   _____

   _____

2. Write the rounded amounts. _____

3. About how many points has Karol earned so far? _____

4. Will 50 points be enough for Karol to get an A? Explain.

   _____

Name _____

Multiplying Whole Numbers by Fractions

Multiply $\frac{1}{4}$ and 3.

One way to solve the problem
is to draw a picture.

Shade in $\frac{1}{4}$ three times.

$$\frac{1}{4} + \frac{1}{4} + \frac{1}{4} = \underline{\frac{3}{4}}$$

$$\frac{1}{4} \times 3 = \frac{3 \times 1}{4} = \underline{\frac{3}{4}}$$

Find each product. Draw a picture to help.

1. $\frac{3}{8} \times 3 =$ _____

2. $\frac{4}{9} \times 2 =$ _____

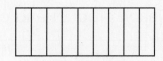

3. $\frac{7}{8} \times 4 =$ _____   **4.** $\frac{1}{3} \times 9 =$ _____

5. $\frac{1}{6} \times 9 =$ _____   **6.** $\frac{3}{7} \times 12 =$ _____

7. $\frac{3}{4} \times 6 =$ _____   **8.** $\frac{2}{5} \times 8 =$ _____

9. $\frac{5}{6} \times 5 =$ _____   **10.** $\frac{3}{10} \times 7 =$ _____

11. $\frac{2}{3} \times 4 =$ _____   **12.** $\frac{1}{6} \times 18 =$ _____

13. $\frac{4}{7} \times 11 =$ _____   **14.** $\frac{5}{8} \times 12 =$ _____

15. $\frac{2}{9} \times 7 =$ _____   **16.** $\frac{3}{11} \times 9 =$ _____

17. $\frac{5}{12} \times 4 =$ _____   **18.** $\frac{3}{4} \times 10 =$ _____

Multiplying Whole Numbers and Mixed Numbers

Step 1 Rewrite. Whole number × denominator + numerator. Write this number over the denominator and remember that the denominator does not change.

$$2\tfrac{3}{4} \times 2\tfrac{2}{3} = \tfrac{11}{4} \times \tfrac{8}{3}$$

Step 2 Simplify. Divide by common factors.

$$\tfrac{11}{{}_1\cancel{4}} \times \tfrac{\cancel{8}^{\,2}}{3}$$

Step 3 Multiply. Rewrite an improper fraction as a mixed number if necessary.

$$\tfrac{11}{1} \times \tfrac{2}{3} = \tfrac{22}{3} \quad 22 \div 3 = \underline{\ 7\ R1\ }, \text{ so } \tfrac{22}{3} = \underline{\ 7\tfrac{1}{3}\ }$$

Follow the steps to find each product and complete the table.

		Step 1: Rewrite	Step 2: Simplify Factors	Step 3: Multiply
1.	$3\tfrac{1}{3} \times 6$	$\tfrac{10}{3} \times 6$	$\tfrac{10}{\cancel{3}_1} \times \tfrac{\cancel{6}^{\,2}}{1}$	$10 \times 2 = 20$
2.	$1\tfrac{3}{4} \times 2$			
3.	$8\tfrac{2}{3} \times 4$			
4.	$1\tfrac{1}{9} \times 3$			
5.	$2\tfrac{1}{2} \times 8$			
6.	$1\tfrac{1}{2} \times 3\tfrac{2}{9}$			
7.	$8\tfrac{1}{4} \times 7\tfrac{1}{3}$			
8.	$4\tfrac{3}{4} \times 3\tfrac{1}{5}$			
9.	$5\tfrac{1}{2} \times 2\tfrac{2}{3}$			
10.	$6\tfrac{3}{5} \times 1\tfrac{7}{8}$			

Name _____

Compare Strategies:
Logical Reasoning/Draw a Picture

Sergie, Alexia, Michael, and Sophie are waiting in line for
movie tickets. Sergie is neither first nor last. Sophie stands
behind Alexis, but Sophie is not last. Alexis is not second
and Sophie is not third. Michael is either first or last

From the information above,
a table can be filled in as
to the right. Use logical
reasoning to complete the
rest of the table.

	Sergei	Alexis	Michael	Sophie
1st	no			no
2nd		no	no	
3rd			no	no
4th	no	no		no

1. How do you know that Alexis never
   can be last and Sophie never can be first?

_____

2. In what order are they in line? Would drawing a picture
   help to answer this problem?

_____

_____

3. Jan, Charlie, Alison, and Victoria each ordered a different sandwich.
   Their orders were turkey, veggie burger, salami, and cheese. No
   one ordered a sandwich that had the same number of syllables as
   his or her name. Alison avoids dairy products and did not order
   the veggie burger. Victoria and Charlie do not like salami. Who
   ordered which sandwich?

Make a table. Use
the clues to fill in
the table.

	Jan	Charlie	Alison	Victoria
Turkey				
Veggie Burger			X	
Salami				
Cheese	X		X	

Name _____

Exploring Division of Fractions

In your book, you used fraction strips to divide whole numbers by fractions. Here is another way to divide by a fraction.

If you wanted to divide 4 into $\frac{1}{6}$'s, you could draw it like this:

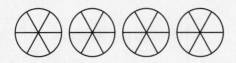

The drawing helps you to see that $4 \div \frac{1}{6} =$ ___24___.

Find each quotient. Draw a picture to help.

1. $4 \div \frac{1}{3} =$ _____

2. $6 \div \frac{1}{6} =$ _____

3. $5 \div \frac{1}{8} =$ _____

4. $7 \div \frac{1}{4} =$ _____

5. $8 \div \frac{1}{2} =$ _____

Exploring Estimating and Measuring Length

In your book you chose appropriate units of measurement to estimate length and height of various items. Here is another way to explore length.

Suppose your friend told you that the distance between the swings and the slide at the park was 10 km. Follow these steps to decide if this is reasonable.

Step 1   Think: How far is 1 km? In your book you learned that four city blocks are about 1 km long. It would probably take you about 10 minutes to walk 1 km. How long would it take to walk 10 km?
<u> 100 min or 1 hr 40 min </u>

Step 2   Visualize: Picture yourself walking from the swings to the slide at the park. How long would it take?
<u> Possible answer: 10 to 15 sec </u>

Step 3   Decide: Is it reasonable that the swings and the slide would be 10 km apart, even in a large park?
<u> no </u>

Decide if each statement is reasonable. Write *yes* or *no*.

1. Marcie said that she saw a butterfly that was 1 m long.   _____

2. Dion said that he caught a fish that was 2 cm long, and it fed his whole family.   _____

3. Claire said that her parrot had a wingspan of 1 km.   _____

4. Joyce's dictionary is 5 cm thick.   _____

5. Keesha's dining room table is 2 m long.   _____

6. Pablo lives 50 km from his aunt's house. He can walk there in about an hour.   _____

7. The caboose on a train is 1 dm long.   _____

Millimeters

Use the following chart to help you know how many times
to multiply or divide by 10 when converting metric units:

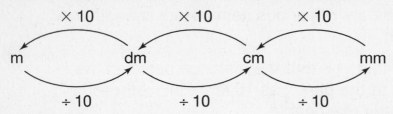

When moving from larger
to smaller units, multiply
by 10.

$$4 \text{ m} = \boxed{} \text{ cm}$$

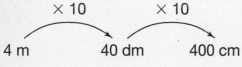

4 m = ___400 cm___

When moving from smaller
to larger units, divide
by 10.

$$400 \text{ m} = \boxed{} \text{ dm}$$

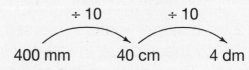

400 mm = ___4 dm___

In the space below each problem, show how you multiplied
or divided by 10 to change each metric unit.

1. 7 m = _____ dm

2. 70 mm = _____ cm

_____

_____

3. 80 m = _____ cm

4. 800 m = _____ dm

_____

_____

5. 8,000 mm = _____ m

6. 80 m = _____ mm

_____

_____

7. 1,500 cm = _____ m

8. 150 m = _____ mm

_____

_____

Centimeters, Meters, and Decimals

Use the diagram to change
from m to cm and from cm to m.

$\times$ 100

m ⟶ cm

$\div$ 100

7 m = [   ] cm   85 cm = [   ] m

7 $\times$ 100 = 700   85 $\div$ 100 = 0.85

7 m = __700__ cm   85 cm = __0.85__ m

Complete.

1. 8 m = [   ] cm

  a. 8 [   ] 100 = _____

  b. 8 m = _____ cm

2. 976 cm = [   ] m

  a. 976 [   ] 100 = _____

  b. 976 cm = _____ m

3. 4 cm = _____ m

4. 800 m = _____ cm

5. 2.16 m = _____ cm

6. 90.8 m = _____ cm

7. 1,882 cm = _____ m

8. 90,000 cm = _____ m

Millimeters, Centimeters, and Decimals

The following diagram shows how to change between cm and mm and between m and cm.

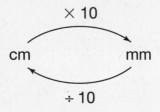

76 mm = [____] cm

76 ÷ 10 = 7.6

76 mm = __7.6__ cm

7 m = [____] cm

7 × 100 = 700

7 m = __700__ cm

Complete.

1. 80 m = [____] cm

    a. 80 _____ 100 = _____

    b. 80 m = _____ cm

2. 976 mm = [____] cm

    a. 976 _____ 10 = _____

    b. 976 mm = _____ cm

3. 14 cm = _____ m

4. 19.87 m = _____ cm

5. 8.32 m = _____ cm

6. 1,437 mm = _____ cm

7. 82 cm = _____ mm

8. 7,321 cm = _____ mm

Name _____

Exploring Perimeter of Polygons

In your book you explored perimeter by measuring shapes.
Here is another way to explore perimeter.

You can use grid paper to help you
find the perimeter of a polygon.

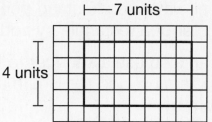

├──7 units──┤

4 units

Count the number of units on each side
of the polygon. Then add.

4 units + 7 units + 4 units + 7 units = __22__ units

The perimeter is __22__ units.

This is a regular polygon. Each side is the
same length. Add the lengths of each side.

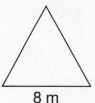

8 m + 8 m + 8 m = __24__

The perimeter is __24__ m.

8 m

_____

Find each perimeter.

1.

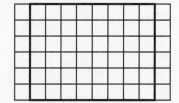

_____

2.

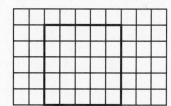

_____

3.

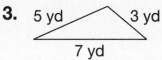

5 yd   3 yd

7 yd

4.

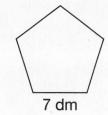

7 dm

_____   _____

Name _____

Exploring Perimeter of Rectangles

In your book you used tables to explore perimeter. Here is
another way to understand perimeter. You can find the
perimeter of a rectangle by adding the lengths of each side.

You can also use a shortcut to find the perimeter of a
rectangle. Just add the length and the width. Then multiply
the sum by 2.

$4 + 3 = 7$

$7 \times 2 = 14$

The perimeter is 14 ft.

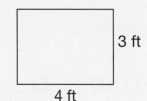

3 ft

4 ft

Find the perimeter of each rectangle.

1. a. $l = $ _____

    b. $w = $ _____

    c. _____ + _____ = _____

    d. _____ × 2 = _____

    e. The perimeter is _____ in.

2 in.

6 in.

2. 1 m

6 m

_____

3. 2 cm

7 cm

_____

4. 4 yd

5 yd

_____

5. 6 in.

16 in.

_____

Name _____

Converting Units to Find Perimeter

Find the perimeter of the rectangle.

Step 1 Change feet to inches. 1 ft = 12 in.
Multiply the number of feet by 12. Add
the number of inches to the result.

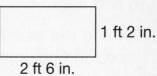

2 ft 6 in. 1 ft 2 in.

2 ft 6 in. = (2 × 12) + 6 = 24 + 6 = __30 in.__
1 ft 2 in. = (1 × 12) + 2 = 12 + 2 = __14 in.__

Step 2 Add length and width and multiply by 2.

(30 + 14) × 2 = 44 × 2 = __88 in.__

Step 3 Convert the answer to larger units.
Change 88 in. to feet by dividing by 12.

88 ÷ 12 = __7 R4__
The remainder amount is the number of inches
left over. So 88 in. = __7 ft 4 in.__

Find the length, width, and perimeter of each rectangle in
inches. Then convert the answer to feet.

1. 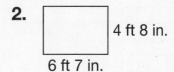 6 ft 9 in.

8 ft 2 in.

a. length: _____

b. width: _____

c. perimeter: _____

d. perimeter in feet and inches:

_____

2. 4 ft 8 in.

6 ft 7 in.

a. length: _____

b. width: _____

c. perimeter: _____

d. perimeter in feet and inches:

_____

3. 2 ft 1 in.

5 ft 4 in.

a. perimeter in inches: _____

b. perimeter in feet and inches:

_____

4. 3 ft 7 in.

5 ft 8 in.

a. perimeter in inches: _____

b. perimeter in feet and inches:

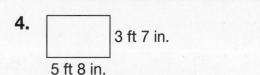

Exploring Area of Rectangles

In your book you drew gardens to find area. Here is another
way to find area.

You can find the area of a rectangle by using
grid paper and counting the square units inside
the rectangle.

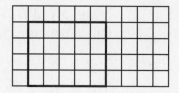

There are 20 squares inside the rectangle.
So, the area of the rectangle is 20 square units.

Area = 20 square units or __20 units^2__

You can also find the area of a rectangle
by multiplying the length by the width.

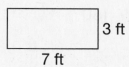

length = 7 ft

width = 3 ft

Area = __7 ft × 3 ft__ = __21 ft^2__

Find the area of each rectangle.

1.

_____

2.

_____

3.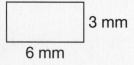

6 mm, 3 mm

_____

4.

9 ft, 7 ft

_____

5.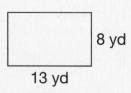

13 yd, 8 yd

_____

6.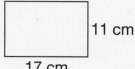

17 cm, 11 cm

_____

Name _____

Decision Making

Kim wants to join a club at her new school. There are
5 clubs she is interested in joining. All the clubs meet
after school.

Kim only has Monday and Wednesday afternoons free.
She wants to join a club with fewer than 40 members.

The table gives information about each club.

Club	Day the Club Meets	Number of Students
Drama	Wednesdays	42
Science	Wednesdays	70
Chess	Tuesdays	20
Computer	Mondays	43
Dance	Mondays	26

Since Kim can only join a club that meets on Monday or
Wednesday, she can't join the __chess club.__

Kim wants to join a club that has fewer than 40 members. Which club
has fewer than 40 members and meets on Monday or Wednesday?

__dance club__

---

1. What if Kim wanted to join a club that met on Mondays
   that had more than 30 members? Which club could she join?

   _____

2. Suppose Terri could join a club that met on Tuesdays
   or Thursdays. Which club could she join?

   _____

3. Pam has a friend in the dance club who gives her a ride
   home after school. Which clubs could Pam join so that
   she can get a ride home with her friend every day?

   _____

Name _____

Exploring Area of Right Triangles

In your book you used the area of a rectangle to help you find the area of a right triangle. Here is another way to find the area of a right triangle.

You can use grid paper to help visualize the area.

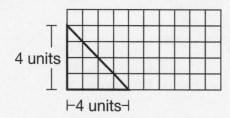

4 units

⊢4 units⊣

You can find the area by counting the squares inside the triangle. Put together the partial pieces to make whole squares.

This triangle covers 8 squares on the grid paper, so its area is 8 units^2.

Another way to find the area of a triangle is to multiply the length of the base by the height. Then divide by 2.

$4 \times 4 = 16$

$16 \div 2 = 8$

The area of the triangle is __8 units^2__.

Find the area of each right triangle.

1.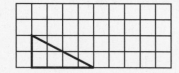

_____

2.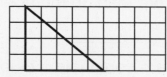

_____

3.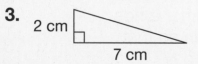

2 cm

7 cm

_____

4.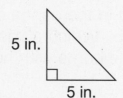

5 in.

5 in.

_____

Exploring Area of Triangles

In your book you explored area of triangles by drawing
triangles inside rectangles. Here is another way to find
the area of triangles.

Use grid paper and the steps below to
help you find the area of triangles.

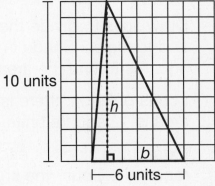

10 units

$\vert$—6 units—$\vert$

Step 1 Count the number of units in the base   base = __6__ units
and in the height.

Step 2 Find the product of the base and the   height = __10__ units
height. Then divide by 2.

$6 \times 10 = 60 \quad 60 \div 2 = 30$

The area of the triangle is __30 units^2__ .

Follow the same steps to find the area of each triangle:

1. a. Count the number of units in the
base and in the height.

base = _____ units   height = _____ units

b. _____ × _____ = _____

c. _____ ÷ 2 = _____

d. A = _____ units^2

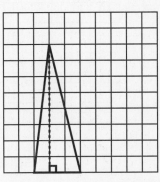

2. a. Count the number of units in the
base and in the height.

base = _____ units   height = _____ units

b. _____ × _____ = _____

c. _____ ÷ 2 = _____

d. A = _____ units^2

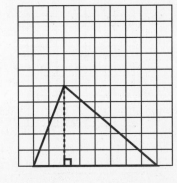

Exploring Area of Other Polygons

In your book you used geoboards and dot paper to explore area of polygons. Here is another way. You can use grid paper to help you find area. Follow these steps.

Step 1   Draw lines to divide the polygon into rectangles and triangles. Shade in rectangles. Count the squares to find the area of each rectangle.

   In this polygon, there is one rectangle. Its area is 12 square units.

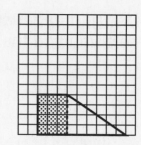

Step 2   Extend the sides of each triangle into a rectangle. Count the squares in each new rectangle and divide by 2 to find the area of each triangle.

   In this polygon, there is one triangle. Its area is 12 square units.

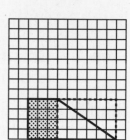

Step 3   Add the areas of the rectangle and triangle to find the area of the polygon.
   12 + 12 = __24 square units__

Follow the same steps to find the area of each polygon.

1.

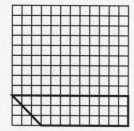

_____ square units

2.

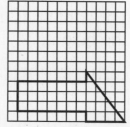

_____ square units

3.

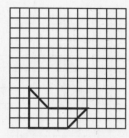

_____ square units

4.

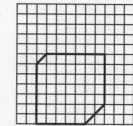

_____ square units

Exploring Area of Parallelograms

In your book you used cutouts and grid paper to explore area of parallelograms. Here is another way to find the area of a parallelogram using dot paper.

Step 1   Call the lower left dot of the parallelogram 0. Count the dots from left to right. The base of the parallelogram is 3 units.

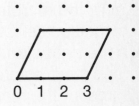

Step 2   Draw a vertical line joining the dots in the middle of the parallelogram. Call the bottom dot 0, and count the dots from bottom to top. The height of the parallelogram is 2 units.

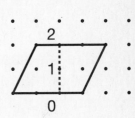

Step 3   Multiply the number of units in the base and the height to find the area.

3 units $\times$ 2 units = 6 square units or 6 units^2.

The area of the parallelogram is ___6 units^2___ .

Follow the steps to find the area of each parallelogram.

1.

_____ units^2

2.

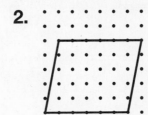

_____ units^2

3.

_____ units^2

4.

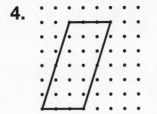

_____ units^2

Exploring Algebra: Balancing Equations

In your book you explored balancing equations by using envelopes and counters. Here is another way to balance equations. Use a balance scale.

Count the marbles on the left side of the balance scale. Count the marbles showing on the right side. You do not know how many marbles are in the bag. Use n to represent the marbles in the bag. Write the problem as an equation.

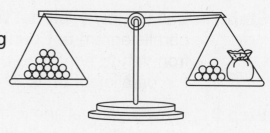

$$16 = 8 + n$$

To make the scales balance, there must be the same number of marbles on each side of the scale. For there to be 16 marbles on the right side, the bag must hold 8 marbles.

$$16 = 8 + \underline{8}$$

$$n = \underline{8}$$

Find the number of marbles in each marble bag.

1.

equation: _____

$n =$ _____

2.

equation: _____

$n =$ _____

3.

equation: _____

$n =$ _____

4.

equation: _____

$n =$ _____

Analyze Strategies: Look for a Pattern

Keesha had her hair cut on Jan. 1st. She had it cut again
on Feb. 2nd and Mar. 6th. If this pattern continues, when will
Keesha's next haircut be?

Use a calendar and make an organized list
to look for a pattern in the numbers.

Month	Date
January	1
February	2
March	6

How many days after
Jan. 1st is Feb. 2nd? __32__

How many days after
Feb. 2nd is Mar. 6th?
(Hint: It is not leap year.) __32__

The pattern is that Keesha has her hair cut every 32 days.

Keesha's next haircut will be 32 days after Mar. 6th,
which is __Apr. 7th.__

---

1. When will Keesha's next 2 haircuts after April 7th be?

_____

Look for a pattern to help solve each problem.

2. On Monday, Skip called Lou at 9:00 A.M. On Tuesday,
he called at 10:30 A.M. On Wednesday, he called at
12:00 noon. If this pattern continues, when will the next
2 phone calls be?

---

3. While playing a game, Fiona took 1 step forward, 2 steps
back, 2 steps forward, 2 steps back, 3 steps forward,
2 steps back. If this pattern continues, what will she do
for the next 2 moves?

Name _____

Exploring Circumference

In your book you used circles drawn with compasses to explore circumference. Here is another way to find circumference.

Find the dot in the center of the circle. Label it A.

Count the number of dots from the center to the edge of the circle. This number is the measure of the radius. In this circle, the radius measures __2 units.__

Multiply the radius by 2. Then multiply the product by π to find the circumference.

Use 3.14 for π.

$2 \times 2 =$ __4__ $4 \times 3.14 =$ __12.56__
The circumference is __12.56 units.__

Find the circumference of each circle.

1.

a. The radius is _____ unit(s).

b. _____ $\times 2 \times 3.14 =$ _____

c. The circumference is

_____ units.

2.

a. The radius is _____ unit(s).

b. _____ $\times 2 \times 3.14 =$ _____

c. The circumference is

_____ units.

3.

a. The radius is _____ unit(s).

b. _____ $\times 2 \times 3.14 =$ _____

c. The circumference is

_____ units.

4.

a. The radius is _____ unit(s).

b. _____ $\times 2 \times 3.14 =$ _____

c. The circumference is

_____ units.

Exploring Solids

In your book you used Power Solids to explore prisms and pyramids. Here is another way to look at these solids.

A **pyramid** is a solid figure whose base is a polygon and whose faces are triangles. Here are some common pyramids.

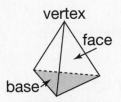

| **Triangular pyramid** | **Rectangular pyramid** | **Pentagonal pyramid** |

A **prism** is a solid figure whose bases are congruent and whose faces are usually rectangles. Here are some common prisms.

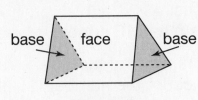 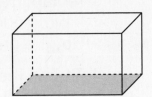 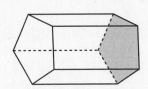

| **Triangular prism** | **Rectangular prism** | **Pentagonal prism** |

Write the name of each solid.

1. _____

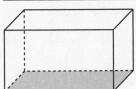

2. _____

3. _____

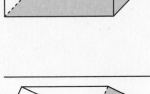

4. _____

Name _____

Exploring Patterns with Solids

In your book you explored patterns by counting the
faces, vertices, and edges of solids. Here is another way
to understand patterns in solids.

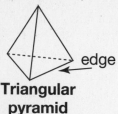

**Triangular
pyramid**

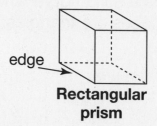

**Rectangular
prism**

To find the number of edges in
a pyramid, count the number
of edges of the base and
multiply by 2.

The triangular pyramid has a
triangular base. Triangles have
3 sides. $3 \times 2 = 6$
So, the pyramid has 6 edges.

To find the number of faces in
a pyramid, count the number
of edges of the base and
add 1.

The triangular pyramid has a
triangular base. Triangles have
3 sides. $3 + 1 = 4$
So, the pyramid has 4 faces.

To find the number of edges in
a prism, count the number of
edges of the base and multply
by 3.

The rectangular prism has a
rectangular base. Rectangles
have 4 edges. $4 \times 3 = 12$
So, the prism has 12 edges.

To find the number of faces
in a prism, count the number
of edges of the base and
add 2.

The rectangular prism has a
rectangular base. Rectangles
have 4 sides. $4 + 2 = 6$
So, the prism has 6 faces.

Find the number of edges and faces of each solid.

1.

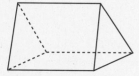

   a. How many
      edges in the base? _____

   b. How many
      edges in the prism? _____

   c. How many faces? _____

2.

   a. How many
      edges in the base? _____

   b. How many
      edges in the pyramid? _____

   c. How many faces? _____

Exploring Nets

In your book you explored nets by drawing nets on dot paper. Here is another way to explore nets.

Trace and cut out the net. Fold it along the dotted lines.

Does this net make a cube?

__yes__

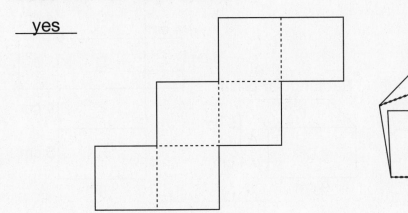

Trace and cut out each net. Fold along the dotted lines.

1. Does this net form a square pyramid? _____

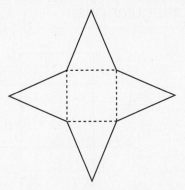

2. Does this net form a cube? _____

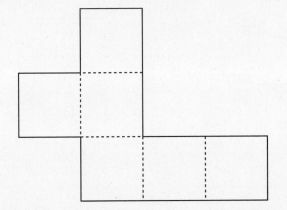

Name _____

Exploring Surface Area

In your book you found the surface area of a solid by taking the figure apart and finding the area of each surface. Here is that method of finding surface area.

Find the area of each face.

Rectangular prism net

Face	Area
A	$5 \times 4 =$ ___20___
B	$5 \times 4 =$ ___20___
C	$4 \times 9 =$ ___36___
D	$5 \times 9 =$ ___45___
E	$4 \times 9 =$ ___36___
F	$5 \times 9 =$ ___45___

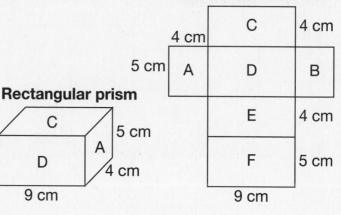

Rectangular prism

Find the sum of the areas. This is the surface area of this rectangular prism. ___202___ cm^2

_____

Complete to find the surface area of the rectangular prism.

1. Area A = $3 \times 5 =$ _____ cm^2

2. Area B = $3 \times \square =$ _____ cm^2

3. Area C = $3 \times 6 =$ _____ cm^2

4. Area D = $5 \times 6 =$ _____ cm^2

5. Area E = $3 \times \square =$ _____ cm^2

6. Area F = $\square \times \square =$ _____ cm^2

7. The sum of the areas = _____.

   The surface area is _____.

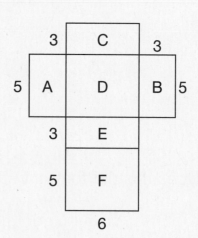

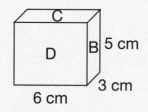

Decision Making

Solve.

1. The cost of wood is $10.00 per 8-ft board, or $1.50 for each foot when the board is less than 8 ft long. How much wood can you afford for:

a. $11? _____

b. $20? _____

c. $27.50? _____

d. $28? _____

2. Each board is 8 ft long. How many inches long is:

a. 1 board? _____

b. 2 boards? _____

c. two 8-ft boards + one 3-ft board? _____

3. Suppose you used 51 in. of wood from an 8-ft board. How many inches of wood would you have left? _____

4. Suppose you used 32 in. of wood from a 4-ft board. How many inches of wood would you have left? _____

5. Suppose you cut lengths of wood measuring 30 in., 21 in., 20 in., and 12 in. from an 8-ft board. Do you have enough wood left to cut another 20-in. length of wood? Explain.

_____

6. Suppose you cut lengths of wood measuring 16 in., 30 in., 11 in., and 13 in. from an 8-ft board. Do you have enough wood left to cut another 2-ft length of wood? Explain.

_____

Ounces, Pounds, and Tons

The ounce (oz), pound (lb), and ton (T) are customary
units used to measure weight.

16 oz = 1 lb   2,000 lb = 1 T

| A comb weighs about 1 oz. | 4 sticks of butter weigh 1 lb. | A small car weighs about 1 T. |

6 T = ☐ lb   48 oz = ☐ lb

A pound weighs less than a ton.   A pound weighs more than
an ounce.

To change to a lesser unit, *multiply*.   To change to a greater unit, *divide*.
1 T = 2,000 lb   1 lb = 16 oz
6 T = 6 × 2,000 = 12,000 lb   48 oz = 48 ÷ 16 = 3 lb

Complete. Check the reasonableness of your answer.

1. 4 lb = ☐ oz
Think: 4 × 16

2. 2 T = ☐ lb
Think: 2 × 2,000

3. 8,000 lb = ☐ T
Think: 8,000 ÷ 2,000

4. 80 oz = ☐ lb
Think: 80 ÷ 16

5. 64 oz = ☐ lb

6. 1 T = ☐ lb

7. 5 lb = ☐ oz

8. 112 oz = ☐ lb

9. 7 T = ☐ lb

10. 12,000 lb = ☐ T

11. Describe how to change 4 lb 7 oz to ounces.

_____

Name _____

Grams and Kilograms

The gram (g) and kilogram (kg) are metric units of mass.
"Kilo" means one thousand, so 1
kilogram = 1,000 grams.

A paper clip has a mass
of about 1 gram.

2.9 kg = ☐ g

A gram is less than a kilogram.

To change to a lesser unit, *multiply*.

1 kg = 1,000 g
2.9 kg = 2.9 × 1,000 = 2,900 g

A math book has a mass
of about 1 kilogram.

67,421 g = ☐ kg

A kilogram is greater than a gram.

To change to a greater unit, *divide*.

1 kg = 1,000 g
67,421 g = 67,421 ÷ 1,000 =
67.421 kg

Use mental math to change to kilograms or grams.

1. 4 kg = ☐ g
Think: 4 × 1,000

2. 2,300 g = ☐ kg
Think: 2,300 ÷ 1,000

3. 45,201 g = ☐ kg
Think: 45,201 ÷ 1,000

4. 7.8 kg = ☐ g
Think: 7.8 × 1,000

5. 5.122 kg = ☐ g

6. 0.567 kg = ☐ g

7. 9,000 g = ☐ kg

8. 78,000 g = ☐ kg

9. 542 g = ☐ kg

10. 50 kg = ☐ g

Name _____

Temperature

How do you calculate differences in temperature?
It depends on where the temperatures fall.

If both temperatures are above or below 0°, <u>ignore any negatives</u> and subtract the lesser number from the greater one.

If one of the temperatures is above 0° and one is below 0°, <u>ignore the negative</u> and add the numbers together.

You can also count the temperature change on a thermometer.

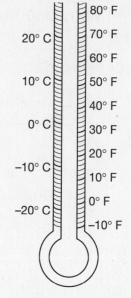

Examples: Find each change in temperature.

10°C to 25°C	−10°C to −25°C	10°C to −10°C
25° − 10° = 15°	25° − 10° = 15°	10° + 10° = 20°

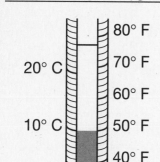 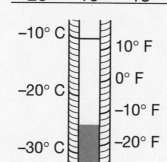 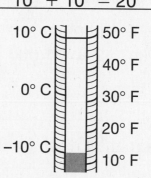

Find each change in temperature.

1. 34°C to 12°C: ☐

2. −34°C to −12°C: ☐

3. −34°C to 12°C: ☐

4. 98°F to 120°F: ☐

5. −1°F to 1°F: ☐

6. 5°C to −15°C: ☐

7. −17°F to −30°F: ☐

8. −1°C to −1°C: ☐

9. 32°F to 212°F: ☐

10. −32°F to 212°F: ☐

11. 40°C to 2°C: ☐

12. 98°F to 102°F: ☐

Name _____

Exploring Volume

In your book you used unit cubes to study volume. Here is another way to explore volume.

Length is the measure along one edge of a shape. *Area* measures a surface. *Volume* measures the space inside.

A box measures 12 in. long × 14 in. wide × 2 in. high.

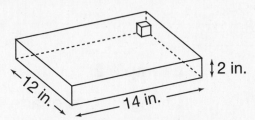

Its volume is the amount of space inside. By finding the product of the length, width, and height, you will find the number of 1-in. cubes that will fit in the box.

12 in. × 14 in. × 2 in. = 336 cubic inches, or 336 in^3.
So, 336 1-in. cubes will fit in the box.

---

1. A water tank measures 15 ft long × 12 ft wide × 8 ft high.

Find the tank's volume. 15 ft × ☐ ft × ☐ ft = ☐ ft^3

2. A brick measures 30 cm long × 10 cm wide × 5 cm high.

a. Find the brick's volume. _____

b. How many 1-cm cubes would you have to glue together to make one brick with the same volume?

_____

Find each volume.

3.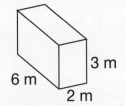

4.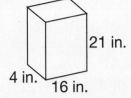

_____ _____

Name _____

Customary Units of Capacity

Some people find it easier to change from one unit
of capacity to another by converting the measurements
to ounces first.

> 1 cup (c) = 8 fl oz
> 1 pint (pt) = 2 c =16 fl oz
> 1 quart (qt) = 2 pt = 32 fl oz
> 1 gallon (gal) = 4 qt = 128 fl oz

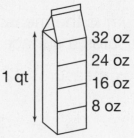

1 qt   32 oz
24 oz
16 oz
8 oz

Example 1:

How many cups are in a quart?

1 qt = 32 fl oz
1 c = 8 fl oz
32 ÷ 8 = 4
So, 4 c = 1 qt.

Example 2:

Change 1 c to quarts.

1 qt = 32 fl oz
1 c = 8 fl oz
32 ÷ 8 = 4
So, 4 c to 1 qt or 1 c = $\frac{1}{4}$ qt.

Complete. Show how you found each answer.

1. How many pints are in a gallon? _____

_____

_____

2. How many cups are in $\frac{1}{2}$ gallon? _____

_____

_____

3. How many cups are in $1\frac{1}{2}$ pints? _____

_____

_____

4. Change 1 c to pints. _____

_____

Metric Units of Capacity

When changing from milliliters (mL) to liters (L), or liters to milliliters, just move the decimal point. Use zeros as "placeholders."

To change from mL to L, you have to divide by 1,000. So, move the decimal point 3 places to the left.

350 mL ⟶ 350. ⟶ 0.35 L

35 mL ⟶ 035. ⟶ 0.035 L

To change from L to mL, you have to multiply by 1,000. So, move the decimal point 3 places to the right.

4.5 L ⟶ 4.500 ⟶ 4,500 mL

0.045 L ⟶ 0.045 ⟶ 45 mL

Change each measurement to liters.

1. 1,700 mL = _____ L

2. 170 mL = _____ L

3. 17 mL = _____ L

4. 50,000 mL = _____ L

5. 3,950 mL = _____ L

6. 625 mL = _____ L

Change each measurement to milliliters.

7. 0.089 L = _____ mL

8. 0.89 L = _____ mL

9. 8.9 L = _____ mL

10. 6.375 L = _____ mL

11. 0.145 L = _____ mL

12. 0.5 L = _____ mL

Name _____

Connecting Volume, Mass, and Capacity

What is the mass of the water in the aquarium?

Step 1   Find the volume.

20 cm × 20 cm × 40 cm = 16,000 cm³

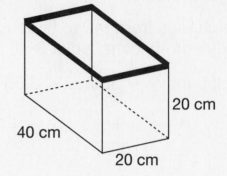

Step 2   Change cm³ to mL.

1 cm³ holds 1 mL.
So, 16,000 cm³ holds 16,000 mL.

Step 3   Change mL to g.

1 mL of water has a mass of 1 g.
So, 16,000 mL has a mass of 16,000 g.

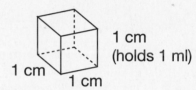

Step 4   Change g to kg.

1 kg = 1,000 g
So, 16,000 g = 16,000 ÷ 1,000 = 16 kg.

The mass of the water in the aquarium is 16 kg.

Find the mass of the water in each aquarium in kilograms.

1.

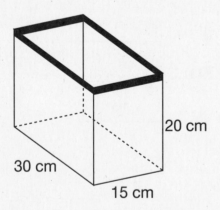

2.

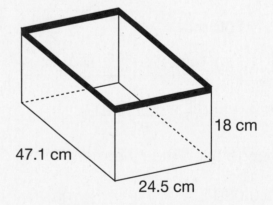

a. Find the volume. _____

b. Change cm³ to mL. _____

c. Change mL to g. _____

d. Change g to kg. _____

a. Find the volume. _____

b. Change cm³ to mL. _____

c. Change mL to g. _____

d. Change g to kg. _____

Compare Strategies: Solve a Simpler Problem/Draw a Picture

Pictures can help you "see" a situation and solve a problem. Solving a Simpler Problem lets you use number patterns.

Rick and Charlie's neighborhood is 7 blocks long by 7 blocks wide. Each block has 8 houses on the north side and 8 houses on the south side. How many houses are in the neighborhood altogether?

Strategy: Solve a Simpler Problem

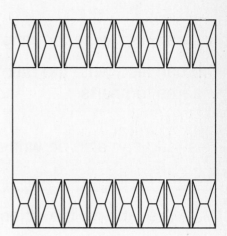

- The neighborhood is 7 blocks long and 7 blocks wide. There are 49 blocks in the neighborhood ($7 \times 7 = 49$). If there was 1 house on each block, there would be 1×49 or 49 houses. If there were 2 houses on each block, there would be 2×49 or 98 houses.

- Each block has 8 houses on the north and 8 houses on the south. There are 16 houses on each block. ($8 + 8 = 16$)

- There are 16 houses on each block, so there are 49×16, or 784 houses.

---

1. Suppose the neighborhood was only 5 blocks long and 5 blocks wide. If each block had 8 houses on the north side and 8 houses on the south, how many houses are there?

_____

2. Lynn created the following pattern with beads. Draw the 25th bead Lynn will use to continue the pattern.

3. Lydia finished her math test after Sean but before Emily. Jane finished the test right after Sean. Mark finished last. Who finished first?

_____

Name _____

Name _____

Name _____

Ratios

A ratio is a pair of numbers that is used to compare quantities. The order in which you show the numbers is important.

You can write the ratio of hearts to squares. There are 2 hearts to 3 squares.

2 hearts and 3 squares
↓   ↓
2   to   3

You can also write the ratio as 2:3 or $\frac{2}{3}$.

You can also write the ratio of squares to hearts.

3 squares and 2 hearts
↓   ↓
_3_   to   _2_

This ratio can also be written as __3:2__ or $\frac{3}{2}$.

Write the ratio for the objects in each picture in 3 ways.

	Words	With a Colon	Fraction

1. diamonds to hearts _____ _____ _____

2. circles to squares _____ _____ _____

3. frowns to smiles _____ _____ _____

Patterns in Ratio Tables

Two ratios that give the same comparison are called equal ratios.

For example, $\frac{1}{3}$ and $\frac{2}{6}$ are equal ratios.

Equal ratios can be thought of as equivalent fractions.

You can use what you know about fractions to find equal ratios. You can multiply or divide the numerator and denominator of a fraction by the same number to find equal ratios.

$\frac{1}{3} = \frac{1 \times 3}{3 \times 3} = \frac{3}{\underline{9}}$ $\frac{3}{9} = \frac{3 \div 3}{9 \div 3} = \frac{1}{\underline{3}}$

You can also use a ratio table to find equal ratios

1	2	3	4	7	10
3	6	9	12	21	30

1. Which pairs of ratios are equal? _____

A. $\frac{2}{3}$ $\frac{4}{9}$ **B.** $\frac{3}{5}$ $\frac{6}{10}$ **C.** $\frac{2}{4}$ $\frac{1}{2}$ **D.** $\frac{3}{8}$ $\frac{9}{16}$

Complete the fractions to make equal ratios.

2. $\frac{2}{5} = \frac{4}{\boxed{}} = \frac{\boxed{}}{15}$

3. $\frac{8}{28} = \frac{4}{\boxed{}} = \frac{\boxed{}}{7}$

Complete each ratio table.

4.

2	4	
5		15

5.

8	4	
28		7

Exploring Equal Ratios

In your book you found equal ratios. Here is another way to find if ratios are equal.

Show the ratios as fractions. Write the fractions in their simplest form. If they match, they are equal ratios.

Are $\frac{2}{4}$, $\frac{4}{8}$, $\frac{8}{16}$, and $\frac{16}{32}$ equal ratios?

$\frac{2}{4} = \frac{1}{2}$ $\qquad\qquad$ $\frac{4}{8} = \frac{1}{2}$

$\frac{8}{16} = \frac{1}{2}$ $\qquad\qquad$ $\frac{16}{32} = \frac{1}{2}$

Yes, they are equal ratios because each one can be written as $\frac{1}{2}$.

---

1. Are $\frac{2}{6}$, $\frac{4}{12}$, $\frac{6}{18}$, and $\frac{8}{24}$ equal ratios? How do you know?

_____

_____

Each ratio on the left is matched by 4 ratios on the right. One of the ratios on the right is not equal to the one on the left. Find the one that is not equal. Write it on the line.

2. $\frac{2}{3}$ $\qquad\qquad$ $\frac{4}{6}$ $\quad$ $\frac{8}{12}$ $\quad$ $\frac{3}{6}$ $\quad$ $\frac{10}{15}$ _____

3. $\frac{1}{5}$ $\qquad\qquad$ $\frac{3}{15}$ $\quad$ $\frac{5}{15}$ $\quad$ $\frac{2}{10}$ $\quad$ $\frac{6}{30}$ _____

4. $\frac{1}{4}$ $\qquad\qquad$ $\frac{9}{27}$ $\quad$ $\frac{9}{36}$ $\quad$ $\frac{7}{28}$ $\quad$ $\frac{6}{24}$ _____

5. $\frac{3}{4}$ $\qquad\qquad$ $\frac{75}{100}$ $\quad$ $\frac{9}{12}$ $\quad$ $\frac{6}{8}$ $\quad$ $\frac{8}{16}$ _____

6. $\frac{2}{5}$ $\qquad\qquad$ $\frac{6}{15}$ $\quad$ $\frac{8}{20}$ $\quad$ $\frac{5}{25}$ $\quad$ $\frac{12}{30}$ _____

7. $\frac{1}{3}$ $\qquad\qquad$ $\frac{3}{7}$ $\quad$ $\frac{3}{9}$ $\quad$ $\frac{4}{12}$ $\quad$ $\frac{5}{15}$ _____

8. $\frac{3}{8}$ $\qquad\qquad$ $\frac{9}{24}$ $\quad$ $\frac{6}{16}$ $\quad$ $\frac{12}{32}$ $\quad$ $\frac{21}{40}$ _____

Name _____

Decision Making

Your scout troop is planning a kickball day. You decide to make a scale drawing of the field area on grid paper to help you plan for the event. The drawing will be proportional to the actual field area.

Some Facts

• The entire field is a square, 90 yards on each side.

• The kickball field is a smaller square in the middle that measures 30 yards on each side.

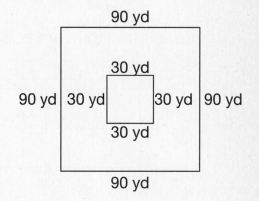

Here are some questions you can ask when you are figuring out dimensions for a scale drawing.

How many yards could 1 square show?
90 and 30 are each divisible by 3, 6, 10, and 15.
Each square could show a length of __3 yd__, __6 yd__, __10 yd__, or __15 yd__.

How many squares show one side of the big field?
Suppose each square shows 3 yards.
90 ÷ 3 = __30__, so 30 squares are needed for each side.

How many squares show one side of the kickball field?
Suppose each square shows 3 yards.
30 ÷ 3 = __10__, so 10 squares are needed for each side.

_____

1. Suppose each square shows 10 yards.
   How many squares show one side of the big field? _____

   The kickball field? _____

2. Suppose each square shows 15 yards.
   How many squares show one side of the big field? _____

   The kickball field? _____

Name _____

Exploring Percent Patterns

In your book you learned how to use patterns to find percents. Here is another way to understand percent patterns.

- All of the fractions in the same column below are equivalent.
- Equivalent fractions are equal to the same percent.

5%	10%	15%	20%	25%	30%
$\frac{5}{100}$	$\frac{10}{100}$	$\frac{15}{100}$	$\frac{20}{100}$	$\frac{25}{100}$	$\frac{30}{100}$
$\frac{1}{20}$	$\frac{2}{20}$	$\frac{3}{20}$	$\frac{4}{20}$	$\frac{5}{20}$	$\frac{6}{20}$
	$\frac{1}{10}$		$\frac{2}{10}$		$\frac{3}{10}$
			$\frac{1}{5}$		
				$\frac{1}{4}$	

Which fractions are equal to 10%? $\frac{10}{100}, \frac{2}{20}, \frac{1}{10}$

Which fractions are equal to 25%? $\frac{25}{100}, \frac{5}{20}, \frac{1}{4}$

You know $\frac{1}{20}$ = 5%. What percent does $\frac{4}{20}$ equal?

$4 \times \frac{1}{20} = \frac{4}{20}$ and $4 \times 5\% = 20\%$ so, $\frac{4}{20} = $ __20%__ .

---

1. Which fractions are equal to 15%? _____

2. Which fractions are equal to 20%? _____

3. What percent does each fraction equal?

a. $\frac{5}{100}$ _____

b. $\frac{20}{100}$ _____

c. $\frac{40}{100}$ _____

d. $\frac{3}{4}$ _____

e. $\frac{3}{5}$ _____

f. $\frac{5}{10}$ _____

Estimating Percent of a Number

The chart below shows when you might use each
benchmark percent when estimating percents.

Problem	To Use Benchmarks	Estimates
11% of 110	10% or $\frac{1}{10}$	10% of 110 is <u>11</u>
24% of 800	25% or $\frac{1}{4}$	25% of 800 is <u>200</u>
35% of 270	$33\frac{1}{3}$ % or $\frac{1}{3}$	$33\frac{1}{3}$ % of 270 is <u>90</u>
46% of 301	50% or $\frac{1}{2}$	50% of 300 is <u>150</u>
62% of 17	$66\frac{2}{3}$ % or $\frac{2}{3}$	$66\frac{2}{3}$ % of 18 is <u>12</u>
77% of 46	75% or $\frac{3}{4}$	75% of 48 is <u>36</u>

Write the percent benchmark you would use to estimate.

1. 76% of 180 _____ **2.** 32% of 33 _____ **3.** 46% of 320 _____

4. 9% of 20 _____ **5.** 63% of 150 _____ **6.** 22% of 80 _____

Estimate.

7. 37% of 36 _____ **8.** 28% of 41 _____

9. 52% of 47 _____ **10.** 71% of 19 _____

11. 68% of 23 _____ **12.** 9% of 24 _____

Finding Percent of a Number

Follow the three examples to learn ways to find 30% of $40.

Example 1

1. Change 30% to a decimal .

$$30\% = 30 \div 100 = 0.30$$

2. Multiply $40 and 0.30.

$$
\begin{array}{r}
\$4\,0 \\
\times \quad 0.3\,0 \\
\hline
\$1\,2.0\,0
\end{array}
$$

Example 2

1. Change 30% to a fraction in simplest form.

$$30\% = 30 \div 100 = \frac{30}{100} = \frac{3}{10}$$

2. Multiply. $\frac{3}{10} \times \$40 = \frac{\$120}{10} = \underline{\ \$12\ }$

Example 3

Use a calculator. Press 30 % × 40 = $\boxed{\ \ 12\ \ }$

Complete to find the percent of each.

1. 45% of 25

a. 45 ÷ 100 = $\boxed{}$

b. $\boxed{}$ × 25 = $\boxed{}$

2. 18% of 55

a. 18 ÷ $\boxed{}$ = $\boxed{}$

b. $\boxed{}$ × $\boxed{}$ = $\boxed{}$

3. 22% of 150

a. $22\% = \frac{22}{100} = \frac{\boxed{}}{50}$

b. $\frac{\boxed{}}{50} \times 150 = \frac{\boxed{}}{\boxed{}} = \boxed{}$

4. 32% of 175

a. $32\% = \frac{\boxed{}}{100} = \frac{\boxed{}}{\boxed{}}$

b. $\frac{\boxed{}}{\boxed{}} \times 175 = \frac{\boxed{}}{\boxed{}} = \boxed{}$

Choose a method. Find the percent of each.

5. 40% of 120 _____

6. 70% of 210 _____

7. 60% of 185 _____

8. 75% of 500 _____

9. 80% of 400 _____

10. 20% of 360 _____

Exploring Fairness

In your book you explored fairness by playing a game.
Here is another way to understand fairness.

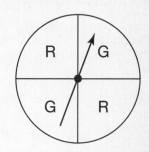

Joe and Larry take turns spinning the spinner.
Joe scores one point if the spinner lands on R.
Larry scores one point if the spinner lands on
G. Is this a fair game?

The outcomes possible are R and G. Each
outcome has the same size space on the spinner,
so each is equally likely to occur.

The game is __fair__.

In a second game, Joe and Larry use another
spinner but keep the same rules.

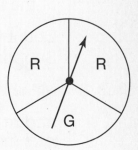

The outcomes possible are R and G. It is
more likely that they will spin R than G
since the R area is larger than the G area. The
outcomes are not equally likely.

The game is __unfair__.

Tell if the outcome is fair or unfair.

If unfair, tell which outcome is more likely.

1. Draw a name out of the hat.

_____

2. Spin the spinner.

_____

3. Choose a marble from the bowl.

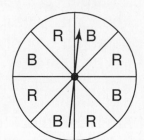

_____

Exploring Predicting from Samples

In your book you explored predictions by doing a letter tally. Here is another way to explore predictions.

A sample is a small set taken from a large set. Predictions can be made about the large set by looking at the sample set.

There are 200 red, green, yellow, and blue marbles in a box. How many red marbles do you predict are in the box?

Follow the steps to find out.

Step 1   Without looking, take a sample of 20 marbles out of the box.

Step 2   Count the number of red marbles in the sample. Suppose there are 8 red marbles.

Step 3   Make a ratio and solve.

$$\text{red marbles in sample} \rightarrow \frac{8}{20} = \frac{n}{200} \leftarrow \text{red marbles in bag}$$
$$\text{total marbles in sample} \rightarrow \phantom{\frac{8}{20}} \phantom{\frac{n}{200}} \leftarrow \text{total marbles in bag}$$

Use equivalent fractions to solve.

$$\frac{8 \times 10}{20 \times 10} = \frac{80}{200}$$

You predict there will be __80__ red marbles in the box of 200 marbles.

---

1. In a sample, 5 out of 20 marbles are yellow. Predict how many yellow marbles are in a box of 100 marbles.

   _____

2. In a sample, 11 out of 25 marbles are green. Predict how many green marbles are in a box of 100 marbles.

   _____

3. In a sample, 9 out of 50 marbles are blue. Predict how many blue marbles are in a box of 400 marbles.

   _____

4. In a sample, 12 out of 100 marbles are black. Predict how many black marbles are in a box of 300 marbles.

   _____

Exploring Predicting from Experiments

In your book you used coins to explore predicting. Here is another way to understand predictions.

You can predict the outcome you expect to happen when you spin the spinner.

If you spin the spinner 9 times, how many times do you predict the outcome will be B?

The spinner is equally likely to land on R, B, or G.

Since there are 3 equal outcomes, 1 out of every 3 spins should be B.

$$\frac{1 \times 3}{3 \times 3} = \frac{3}{9}$$ ___3___ out of every 9 spins should be B.

To see if your predictions are correct, you can experiment by spinning the spinner and recording the results in a table. The more times the experiment is performed, the closer the results will be to the predicted outcomes.

---

1. Each face of the number cube has one of the numbers 1, 2, 3, 4, 5, or 6. In 20 tosses, how many times do you expect an even number to be rolled?

_____

2. Toss the number cube 20 times. Complete the tally table.

Outcome	Tally	Total	Outcome	Tally	Total
1			4		
2			5		
3			6		

3. Did the experiment support your prediction?

_____

_____

Analyze Strategies:
Make an Organized List

A diner has a platter special of one meat and one vegetable for $2.99. You have a choice of 3 meats and 4 vegetables. How many choices are there for the platter?

You can find out by making an organized list. A tree diagram is one way to make an organized list.

Platter Special	
1 Meat	**1 Vegetable**
beef	spinach
pork	asparagus
chicken	zucchini
	egg plant

Choose a letter for each meat and vegetable. Match each meat with each of the vegetables.

Meat	Vegetable	Platter
	S	BS
	A	BA
B	Z	BZ
	E	BE
	S	PS
	A	PA
P	Z	PZ
	E	PE
	S	CS
	A	CA
C	Z	CZ
	E	CE

Count the number of platters. There are __12__ .

_____

Use a tree diagram to solve the problem.

The school cafeteria serves sandwiches. You can choose ham, salami, or turkey, on whole wheat, rye, or 7-grain bread. How many sandwich combinations are there?

_____

_____

_____

Expressing Probabilities as Fractions

The spinner is divided into 8 equal parts.

There are 8 possible outcomes. Since 3 parts have the letter C, 3 of the 8 outcomes are C's. The probability of the spinner stopping on C is 3 out of 8 or $\frac{3}{8}$.

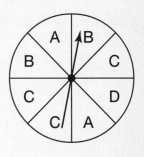

Two out of the 8 possible outcomes are B's, so the probability of stopping on B is $\frac{2}{8}$, or in simplest form, $\frac{1}{4}$.

The probability of stopping on A is __2__ out of 8, or $\frac{2}{8}$ or $\frac{1}{4}$.

The probability of stopping on D is __1__ out of 8, or $\frac{1}{8}$.

Give the probability of each outcome as a fraction. Simplify.

1. What is the probability the spinner will stop on

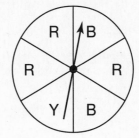

   a. R? _____

   b. B? _____

   c. Y? _____

2. Toss a cube with these faces. What is the probability of rolling

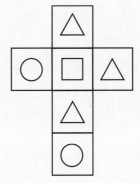

   a. a triangle? _____

   b. a circle? _____

   c. a square? _____

Name _____

Exploring Expected and Experimental Results

The spinner is divided into 4 equal parts. There are 4 equally likely possible outcomes.

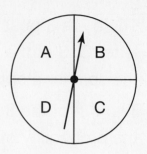

So the probability of each of the 4 outcomes is $\frac{1}{4}$.

Suppose the spinner is spun 20 times.

To find the **expected results** for getting A in 20 spins, multiply the probability of getting A by the number of spins.

$\frac{1}{4} \times 20 =$ ___5___

You should expect to get A, 5 times.

_____

For each spinner, find the probability for the outcome. Then find the expected results.

1. Outcome: 2

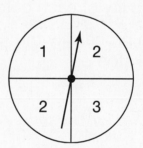

Probability: _____

Expected results for 50 spins:

_____ $\times$ 50 = _____

2. Outcome: C

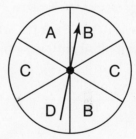

Probability: _____

Expected results for 90 spins:

_____ $\times$ 90 = _____

Reading Graphs

The graph on the left is called a **bar graph**.

The graph on the right is called a **pictograph**.

Running Speed of Land Animals

Animals: Cheetah, Horse, Rabbit, Human, Squirrel
Speed in m.p.h.: 0 10 20 30 40 50 60 70

Endangered Species in the U.S.

Mammals ○ ○ ○ ○ ○ ◖
Fish ○ ○ ○ ○ ○ ○ ◖
Insects ○ ○

○ =10 species
◖ = 5 species

This graph shows the speeds of different animals. Look at the bar labeled "Cheetah". Line up the bar with the numbers for speed. The graph tells you that cheetahs run at __70 m.p.h.__

This graph shows the number of endagered species in the United States. Each symbol represents 10 species. So, to find out how many species of insects are endangered, multiply 2 × 10 = __20__ .

Use the graph on the left to answer **1–3**.

1. Which animal runs at about 35 m.p.h.? __rabbit__
2. Which animal on the graph is the slowest? __squirrel__
3. Which animals run faster than humans? __cheetah, horse, rabbit__

Use the graph on the right to answer **4–6**.

4. How many species of mammals in the U.S. are endangered?
   __55 species__
5. How many species of fish in the U.S. are endangered?
   __65 species__
6. How many more species of mammals are endangered than species of insects? __35__

Reading Line Graphs

You can read a graph to get information. **Line graphs** show change over a period of time. This graph shows the average temperature in Minneapolis.

This is the vertical axis.

Average Temperature in Minneapolis

Temperature in °F: 0° 10° 20° 30° 40° 50° 60° 70° 80°
Month: January April July October

This is the horizontal axis.

What is the average temperature in Minneapolis in January?

Step 1 Find January on the horizontal axis.

Step 2 Trace a straight line from January until you reach a point on the graph. Trace another line from the point to the vertical axis to find the temperature. __11°F__

Coordinates You can show the temperature in January by writing this coordinate: (January, 11°F). The data from the horizontal axis always goes first.

Use the line graph to answer **1–5**.

1. What is the average temperature in Minneapolis in April? __46°F__
2. What is the average temperature in Minneapolis in October? __49°F__
3. Write the coordinates to show the average temperature in July. __(July, 74°F)__
4. In which month shown is the average temperature the lowest? __January__
5. Which two months have average temperatures that are about the same? __April and October__

Reading Stem-and-Leaf Plots

A **stem-and-leaf** plot is a way to organize data. You can use it to organize the data shown.

The numbers on the left are the tens digits.

Stem	Leaf
2	3 9 5 8
1	9 8

The numbers on the right are the ones digits.

To show 19 and 18 in the stem-and-leaf plot, write the ones digit across from the tens digit, 1.

The sleeping habits of the five animals that sleep the most in a typical day are shown in the stem-and-leaf plot below. Use the stem-and-leaf plot to answer **1–4**.

Hours of Sleep

Stem	Leaf
②	2 ⓪
1	6 9 9 _5_

1. Circle the numbers that show 20 hours on the stem-and-leaf plot.
2. Suppose another animal sleeps 15 hours. Show this data in the stem-and-leaf plot.
3. How many animals sleep 20 hours? __1 animal__
4. What is the greatest number of hours shown in the table?
   __22 hours__
5. Armadillos and opossums sleep the same number of hours. The number of hours they sleep is shown in the stem-and-leaf plot. How many hours do they sleep daily?
   __19 hours__

Range, Mode, and Median

You can use data to find the range, mode, and median.

The **range** is the difference between the least and the greatest numbers.

Price of Portable Stereos

$25 $40 $75 $100 $125
Price

What is the greatest price? __$125__
What is the least price? __$25__
greatest price – least price = __$100__
The range is __$100__ .

The **mode** is the number that occurs the most.
Which price occurs most often in the plot? __$40__
This number is the mode.

The **median** is the number that is exactly in the middle, when the data is arranged in order from least to greatest.

$25 $40 $40 $40 $40 $75 $75 $75 $100 $100 $125

Cross off numbers on either side until you find the middle.
Which price is exactly in the middle? __$75__
This number is the median.

If there is an even number of data items, the median is exactly halfway between the two middle numbers. You can add the two middle numbers and divide by 2 to get the median.

Use the line plot to answer **1–3**.

1. What is the range? __4 hours__
2. What is the mode? __1 hour__
3. What is the median? __2 hours__

Hours Spent Reading Over the Weekend

Hours: 0 1 2 3 4

165

Name _____

Another Look
1-5

Introduction to the Problem Solving Guide

This graph shows the number of students who prefer different sports.

How many students did not select football or baseball?

Student Survey of Favorite Sports

Sports		Number of Students
Basketball		
Baseball		
Football		
Tennis		
Soccer		

0 2 4 6 8 10 12
Number of Students

What do you know?   The number of students who prefer each sport.

What do you need to find out?   The number of students who prefer sports other than football or baseball.

How can you find out?   Find the total number of people who prefer all the other sports.

How many students picked basketball? __10 students__

tennis? __4 students__   soccer? __7 students__

Add.

__10__ (basketball) + __4__ (tennis) + __7__ (soccer) = __21__

(total not including football or baseball)

---

1. How many more students like football than baseball and tennis combined?

   a. How many students prefer football? __12 students__

   b. How many students prefer baseball? __5 students__

   c. How many students prefer tennis? __4 students__

   d. How many students prefer baseball and tennis combined? __9 students__

   e. What is the difference between the number of students who prefer football and the number who prefer baseball and tennis combined?
   __3 students__

Use with pages 18–19. **5**

Name _____

Another Look
1-6

Analyze Word Problems: Choose an Operation

Joseph watched Mrs. O'Brien's children for 4 hours. He was paid a total of $12 to babysit. How much was he paid per hour?

What do you know? He was paid $12 for 4 hours of babysitting.

What do you need to find out? How much he was paid an hour.

What is the key action? Making equal groups

What operation will you use? Division. $12 ÷ 4 = $3.

What is the answer? Joseph was paid $3 per hour.

How can you check your answer?

Multiply my answer by the hours he worked. The amount should be the amount he was paid. $3 × 4 hours = $12.

Suzanna made cookies for her school's bake sale. She baked 2 dozen chocolate chip and 3 dozen peanut butter cookies. How many dozen cookies did she bake in all?

1. What do you know?
   She made 2 dozen of one cookie and 3 dozen of another.

2. What do you need to find out?
   how many dozen she made in all

3. What is the key action? combining groups

4. What operation will you use? addition; 2 + 3 = 5

5. What is the answer? 5 dozen cookies in all

6. How can you check your answer?
   Subtract one of the addends from the sum to find the other
   addend. 5 − 2 = 3

6 Use with pages 20–21.

Name _____

Another Look
1-7

Exploring Algebra: What's the Rule?

In your book, you answered questions to find the rule for a table. Here is another way to find the rule.

Ask yourself: "What can I do to 2 to make 4?"

A	B
2	4
3	6
5	10
7	14
9	18

2 + 2 = 4

2 × 2 = 4

Then ask: "Which operation will work for the next pair?"

3 + 2 ≠ 6

3 × 2 = 6

To write the rule using a variable, replace the number from the table (3) with a variable (*n*).

So, change 3 × 2 to *n* × 2.

To write the rule in words, just describe the operation: multiply by 2.

A	B
1	5
6	10
8	12
10	14
13	17

1. a. What can you do to 1 to make 5? 1 + 4 = 5, 1 × 5 = 5

   b. Which operation will work for the next pair?
   addition; 6 + 4 = 10

   c. Write the rule using a variable. *n* + 4

   d. Write the rule using words. Add 4.

   e. Does the rule work for all the pairs in the table? yes

Use with pages 22–23. **7**

Name _____

Another Look
1-8

Scales and Bar Graphs

Make a **bar graph** for the data in this table.

Visitors to Historic Museums in 1995	
Boot Hill Museum (Dodge City, KS)	124,000
Pioneer Arizona Living History Museum (Phoenix, AZ)	47,000
Shelburne Museum (Shelburne, VT)	155,000
St. Augustine Historic District (St. Augustine, FL)	60,000

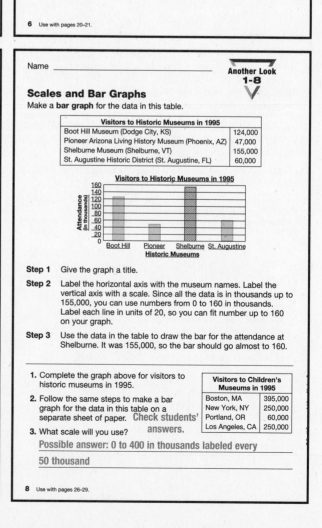

Visitors to Historic Museums in 1995

Step 1   Give the graph a title.

Step 2   Label the horizontal axis with the museum names. Label the vertical axis with a scale. Since all the data is in thousands up to 155,000, you can use numbers from 0 to 160 in thousands. Label each line in units of 20, so you can fit number up to 160 on your graph.

Step 3   Use the data in the table to draw the bar for the attendance at Shelburne. It was 155,000, so the bar should go almost to 160.

---

1. Complete the graph above for visitors to historic museums in 1995.

2. Follow the same steps to make a bar graph for the data in this table on a separate sheet of paper. Check students' answers.

3. What scale will you use?
   Possible answer: 0 to 400 in thousands labeled every
   50 thousand

Visitors to Children's Museums in 1995	
Boston, MA	395,000
New York, NY	250,000
Portland, OR	60,000
Los Angeles, CA	250,000

8 Use with pages 26–29.

166

Another Look
1-9

Exploring Making Line Graphs

In your book, you explored making **line graphs**. Here is another way to make line graphs.

Use what you learned about making bar graphs to help you make line graphs.

Step 1 Make a bar graph to show the data in the table.

Step 2 Change the bar graph into a line graph by drawing lines to connect the tops of each bar.

Day of Storm	Depth of Snow (in inches)
1	4
2	6
3	5
4	8
5	10
6	9

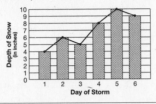

1. Make a bar graph that shows the data in the table.

2. Change the bar graph to a line graph by connecting the tops of each bar.

Day of Storm	Depth of Snow (in inches)
1	6
2	4
3	8
4	9
5	7
6	8

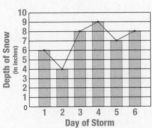

Another Look
1-10

Exploring Making Stem-and-Leaf Plots

In your book you made **stem-and-leaf plots**. Here is another way to make stem-and-leaf plots.

The stem-and-leaf plot is like a bar graph made of numbers. It helps you see what group of numbers makes up the greatest part of the data.

Average Speed in Miles per Hour			
Cat	30	Lion	50
Cape Hunting Dog	45	Pig	11
Cheetah	70	Rabbit	35
Elephant	25	Squirrel	12
Grizzly Bear	30	Zebra	40
Human	28		

Stem	Leaf
7	0
6	
5	0
4	5 0
3	0 0 5
2	5 8
1	1 2

Step 1 Draw a large T. Write "Stem" at the top of the left column and "Leaf" at the top of the right column.

Step 2 Write the numbers in the tens place in order from greatest to least in the left column. This is the stem.

Step 3 Make the leaves. Write the ones digits in the row next to their corresponding tens digit in the right column.

1. Make a stem-and-leaf plot for the data in the table below.

Average Life Span in Years			
Rhinoceros (white)	20	Red Fox	7
Rhinoceros (black)	15	Guinea Pig	10
Rhesus Monkey	15	Rabbit	5
Polar Bear	20	Squirrel	10
Lion	15	Chipmunk	6
Horse	20	Giraffe	10
Grizzly Bear	25	Leopard	12
Gorilla	20	Pig	10
Dog	12	Kangaroo	7
Cat	12	Opossum	1
Camel	12	Mouse	3
Black Bear	18		

Stem	Leaf
2	0 0 0 0 5
1	0 0 0 0 2 2 2 2 5 5 5 8
0	1 3 5 6 7 7

Order in leaves may vary.

Another Look
1-11

Analyze Strategies:
Use Logical Reasoning

Alberto, Casey, Edgar, and Glenda each do best in one of four school subjects: spelling, science, reading, and math. Casey was the winner of the school spelling bee. Alberto doesn't like to read. Edgar hopes to become a scientist. Given these interests, which student likes to read.

What information is given directly? <u>Casey won the spelling bee and Edgar wants to become a scientist.</u>

Cross out spelling and science in the list of subjects.

<u>Since Alberto hates to read, the only other subject left is math.</u>

Cross out math in the list of subjects.

<u>Glenda must be the one who likes to read.</u>

There are four members of different ages on the Southside Bowling Team. They always bowl according to their age, oldest to youngest. Allison is not the oldest team member. Katie bowls second. Sophie does not bowl last. Georgia is almost the youngest team member. In what order does the team bowl?

1. What information is given directly? <u>Katie bowls second.</u>

2. Who bowls second? <u>Katie</u>

3. What clues help you rule out who bowls last?
<u>Sophie does not bowl last. Georgia is almost the youngest team member.</u>

4. Who bowls last? <u>Allison</u>

5. What clue helps you decide who bowls third?
<u>Georgia is almost the youngest team member.</u>

6. Who bowls third? <u>Georgia</u>

7. Who bowls first? <u>Sophie</u>

Another Look
2-1

Exploring a Million

In your book you used place-value blocks and grid paper to explore a million. Here's another way to understand millions.

A roll of dimes is worth $10.00. It holds 100 dimes. How many dimes are there in 5 rolls?

5 rolls of 100 dimes each is the same as 5 hundreds or <u>500 dimes</u>.

50 rolls of 100 dimes each is the same as 50 hundreds or 5 thousands or <u>5,000</u>.

500 rolls of 100 dimes each is the same as 500 hundreds or 50 thousands or <u>50,000</u>.

5,000 rolls of 100 dimes each is the same as 5,000 hundreds or 500 thousands or <u>500,000</u>.

50,000 rolls of 100 dimes each is the same as 50,000 hundreds or 5,000 thousands or 5 millions or <u>5,000,000</u>.

How many dimes are in each number of rolls?

1. 8 rolls = <u>8</u> rolls of 100 dimes = <u>8</u> hundreds = <u>800</u> dimes

2. 12 rolls = <u>12</u> rolls of 100 dimes = <u>12</u> hundreds = <u>1,200</u> dimes

3. 20 rolls = <u>20</u> hundreds = <u>2,000</u> dimes

4. 87 rolls = <u>87</u> hundreds = <u>8,700</u> dimes

5. 120 rolls = <u>120</u> hundreds = 12 thousands = <u>12,000</u> dimes

6. 370 rolls = <u>370</u> hundreds = <u>37</u> thousands = <u>37,000</u> dimes

7. 700 rolls = <u>700</u> hundreds = <u>70</u> thousands = <u>70,000</u> dimes

8. 1,600 rolls = <u>1,600</u> hundreds = 160 thousands = <u>160,000</u> dimes

9. 5,000 rolls = <u>5,000</u> hundreds = <u>500</u> thousands = <u>500,000</u> dimes

10. 20,000 rolls = <u>20,000</u> hundreds = 2,000 thousands = <u>2</u> millions = <u>2,000,000</u> dimes

Name _____

Place Value Through Millions

Here's another way to use a place-value chart to read and write numbers.

Here is a place-value chart for the number 743,162,905.

Millions			Thousands			Ones		
hundreds	tens	ones	hundreds	tens	ones	hundreds	tens	ones
7	4	3	1	6	2	9	0	5

Each group of three digits is called a period. Each period has a name. When you read and write the word form of numbers, you include the period name after each period, except the ones period.

Word form seven hundred forty-three <u>million</u>, one hundred sixty-two <u>thousand</u>, nine hundred five

Standard form <u>743,162,905</u>

Use the chart to help you write the word form for each number. Underline the period name as above.

1. 649,207,358

six hundred forty-nine <u>million</u>, two hundred seven <u>thousand</u>,

three hundred fifty-eight

2. 813,960,527

eight hundred thirteen <u>million</u>, nine hundred sixty <u>thousand</u>,

five hundred twenty-seven

3. 7,645,002

seven <u>million</u>, six hundred forty-five <u>thousand</u>, two

---

Name _____

Exploring Place-Value Relationships

The expression 10^4 means $10 \times 10 \times 10 \times 10$.

The number 10 is called the base.

The number 4 is called the exponent.

10^4 is read as 10 to the 4th power.

The exponent tells how many 10s to multiply.

So, 10^4 is the product of four 10s.

$10^4 = 10 \times 10 \times 10 \times 10 = $ <u>10,000</u>

Write the value of each number.

1. $10^2 = 10 \times \boxed{10} = $ <u>100</u>

2. $10^5 = $ <u>$10 \times 10 \times 10 \times 10 \times 10$</u> = <u>100,000</u>

3. $10^3 = $ <u>$10 \times 10 \times 10$</u> = <u>1,000</u>

4. $10^6 = $ <u>$10 \times 10 \times 10 \times 10 \times 10 \times 10$</u> = <u>1,000,000</u>

Write each number using exponents.

5. $1,000 = 10 \times 10 \times 10 = 10^{\boxed{3}}$

6. $10,000 = $ <u>$10 \times 10 \times 10 \times 10$</u> = <u>$10^4$</u>

7. $1,000,000 = $ <u>$10 \times 10 \times 10 \times 10 \times 10 \times 10$</u> = <u>$10^6$</u>

8. $100 = $ <u>10×10</u> = <u>10^2</u>

9. In 10^7 the number <u>10</u> is the base and the number <u>7</u> is the exponent.

10. What do you notice about the number of zeros in the number and exponent?

<u>Possible answers: The exponent is equal to the number of</u>

<u>zeros in the product; the exponent is equal to the number of</u>

<u>factors of 10.</u>

Name _____

Place Value Through Billions

Use the place-value chart to read and write numbers.

Billions			Millions			Thousands			Ones		
hundreds	tens	ones	hundreds	tens	ones	hundreds	tens	ones	hundreds	ten	ones
2	8	6	3	7	9	5	4	0	0	0	0

This place-value chart shows a 12-digit number.

The number has 4 periods.

In standard form, each period, except the ones, is followed by a comma.

Standard form <u>286,379,540,000</u>

In word form, each period, except the ones, is followed by the period name.

Word form two hundred eighty-six <u>billion</u>, three hundred seventy-nine <u>million</u>, five hundred forty <u>thousand</u>

The period names have been underlined.

Use the place-value chart to help you write each number in standard form or word form.

1. thirty-four billion <u>34,000,000,000</u>

2. six hundred billion, seventy million <u>600,070,000,000</u>

3. eight billion, eighty million, eight hundred thousand <u>8,080,800,000</u>

4. 4,030,400,050 = <u>four</u> billion, <u>thirty</u> million, <u>four hundred</u> thousand, <u>fifty</u>

5. 15,700,005,009 = fifteen <u>billion</u>, seven hundred <u>million</u>, five <u>thousand</u>, nine

6. 301,417,900,770 = three hundred one <u>billion</u>, four hundred seventeen million, nine hundred <u>thousand</u>, <u>seven hundred</u> seventy

---

Name _____

Comparing and Ordering

In 1993 the Port of Cleveland, Ohio handled 14,083,014 tons of cargo and the Port of Freeport, Texas handled 14,024,604 tons.

You can compare the two amounts using a place-value chart.

	Millions			Thousands			Ones		
	hundreds	tens	ones	hundreds	tens	ones	hundreds	tens	ones
Cleveland Ohio	1	4	0	8	3	0	1	4	
Freeport Texas	1	4	0	2	4	6	0	4	

First, look at the numbers in the chart. Start on the left, the millions column, and compare digits. Which column is the first place that the numbers differ? <u>ten thousands</u>

Since 8 ten thousands > 2 ten thousands

then $14,0\boxed{8}3,014$ <u>></u> $14,0\boxed{2}4,604$.

Write >, <, or = to complete. Use place-value charts. Circle the first digit in each number that helps you determine which number is greater.

1. $37,\boxed{0}48$ < $37,\boxed{1}84$ **2.** $2\boxed{1}7,906$ < $2\boxed{7}1,906$

3. $4,0\boxed{0}0,056$ < $4,0\boxed{1}0,065$ **4.** $54\boxed{2},340$ > $54\boxed{0},240$

To order a series of numbers, compare two numbers at a time. Continue comparing until you find the least.

Order these numbers from least to greatest.

5. 315,297   351,972   35,998   315,792

<u>35,998; 315,297; 315,792; 351,972</u>

Rounding Numbers

Round 457,928 to the nearest ten thousand using a place-value chart. Copy the number into the chart below. Circle the number in the place to which you are rounding.

Thousands			Ones		
hundreds	tens	ones	hundreds	tens	ones
4	(5)	7 ,	9	2	8
4	6	0 ,	0	0	0
A	**B**	**C**	**C**	**C**	**C**

A. Find the number or numbers to the left of the number you circled. Copy it or them onto the answer lines below the numbers.

B. Find the number to the right of the circled number. If that number is 5 or more, add 1 to the circled number and write it below the circled number. If it is 4 or less, do not change the circled number. Copy the same number on the answer line below the circled number.

C. Write zeros on the answer lines to the right of this number. This is the rounded number. → __460,000__

1. Round 735,934 to the nearest hundred thousand. Circle the number in the place to which you are rounding.

Thousands			Ones		
hundreds	tens	ones	hundreds	tens	ones
(7)	3	5 ,	9	3	4
7	0	0 ,	0	0	0

2. Round 48,148,921 to the nearest million.

Millions			Thousands			Ones		
hundreds	tens	ones	hundreds	tens	ones	hundreds	tens	ones
	4	8 ,	1	4	8 ,	9	2	1
	4	8 ,	0	0	0 ,	0	0	0

Tenths and Hundredths

In the book you used place-value blocks to show decimals. You can also use a grid.

Decimal **1.23**

Identify the place values.

How many ones? __1__

How many tenths? __2__

How many hundredths? __3__

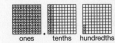
ones tenths hundredths

Shade in the grids to show each decimal. Then answer the questions.

1. 0.87
   a. How many tenths? __8__
   b. How many hundredths? __7__

2. 1.45
   a. How many ones? __1__
   b. How many tenths ? __4__
   c. How many hundredths? __5__

3. 2.64
   a. How many ones? __2__
   b. How many tenths? __6__
   c. How many hundredths? __4__

Exploring Equivalent Decimals

In your book you used place-value blocks and grid paper to explore equivalent decimals. Here is another way to understand equivalent decimals.

You can use pennies and dimes to show decimals.

1 penny is one hundredth of a dollar. 1 dime is 1 tenth of a dollar.

0.07 is 7 hundredths

0.7 is 7 tenths

These two amounts are not the same, so they are not equivalent.

0.20 is 20 hundredths

0.2 is 2 tenths

These two amounts are the same, so they are equivalent.

1. a. Write a decimal to describe each money amount.

 __0.03__   __0.3__

   b. Are the two decimals equivalent? __No__

Draw pennies and dimes to show each amount. Then circle equivalent or not equivalent.

2. 0.05 and 0.50

equivalent (not equivalent)

3. 0.10 and 0.1

(equivalent) not equivalent

Thousandths

You can use place value to help you write decimals. Just remember that the last digit of the decimal should be in the place named.

Write 13 thousandths in decimal form.

The last digit of this number is in the thousandths place. So, write the 3 in the thousandths place. Write the 1 in front of it. Fill in the rest with zeros.

$\underline{0} . \underline{0}\ \underline{1}\ \underline{3}$
ones tenths hundredths thousandths

Write 4 hundredths in decimal form.

The last digit of this number is in the hundredths place. So, write the 4 in the hundredths place. Fill in the rest with zeros.

$\underline{0} . \underline{0}\ \underline{4}$
ones tenths hundredths

Write each number in decimal form.

1. 16 hundredths

$\underline{0} . \underline{1}\ \underline{6}$
ones tenths hundredths thousandths

2. 2 hundredths

$\underline{0} . \underline{0}\ \underline{2}$
ones tenths hundredths thousandths

3. 24 thousandths

$\underline{0} . \underline{0}\ \underline{2}\ \underline{4}$
ones tenths hundredths thousandths

4. 157 thousandths

$\underline{0} . \underline{1}\ \underline{5}\ \underline{7}$
ones tenths hundredths thousandths

5. 3 thousandths

$\underline{0} . \underline{0}\ \underline{0}\ \underline{3}$
ones tenths hundredths thousandths

6. 40 thousandths

$\underline{0} . \underline{0}\ \underline{4}\ \underline{0}$
ones tenths hundredths thousandths

7. 6 and 19 thousandths

$\underline{6} . \underline{0}\ \underline{1}\ \underline{9}$
ones tenths hundredths thousandths

8. 5 tenths

$\underline{0} . \underline{5}$
ones tenths hundredths thousandths

Decimals on the Number Line

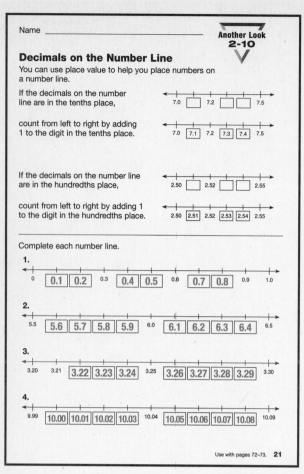

Name _____

Another Look 2-10

Decimals on the Number Line

You can use place value to help you place numbers on a number line.

If the decimals on the number line are in the tenths place,

count from left to right by adding 1 to the digit in the tenths place.

If the decimals on the number line are in the hundredths place,

count from left to right by adding 1 to the digit in the hundredths place.

Complete each number line.

1.

2.

3.

4.

Use with pages 72–73. **21**

Name _____

Another Look 2-11

Exploring Comparing and Ordering Decimals

In your book you used 10 × 10 grids to compare and order decimals. Here's another way to compare decimals.

Compare 0.34 and 0.39

You can see that 0.34 < 0.39 because it is farther to the left on the number line than 0.39.

Use the number lines to compare each pair of numbers. Write >, <, or =.

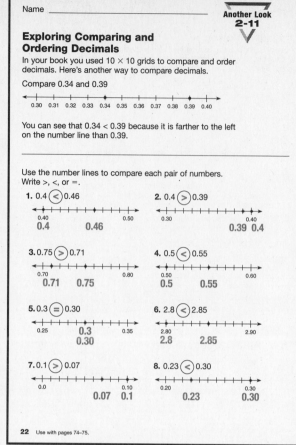

1. 0.4 < 0.46   2. 0.4 > 0.39

3. 0.75 > 0.71   4. 0.5 < 0.55

5. 0.3 = 0.30   6. 2.8 < 2.85

7. 0.1 > 0.07   8. 0.23 < 0.30

22 Use with pages 74–75.

Name _____

Another Look 2-12

Rounding Decimals

Round 0.592 to the nearest tenth.

Step 1 Circle the digit in the tenths place.   0.⑤92

Step 2 Look at the digit to the right of the circled digit.

If the digit is:	Do this:
less than 5	keep the circled digit as it is
5 or greater	add 1 to the circled digit

Step 3 Drop all digits to the right of the circled digit and write the rounded number.

0.592 rounded to the nearest tenth is __0.6__ .

Circle the digit in the given place.

1. 2.④57
tenths

2. 0.7②2
hundredths

3. 0.②45
tenths

4. 1.3④3
hundredths

Round each number to the given place.

5. 2.457
tenths
__2.5__

6. 0.722
hundredths
__0.72__

7. 0.245
tenths
__0.2__

8. 1.343
hundredths
__1.34__

9. 0.764
tenths
__0.8__

10. 0.764
hundredths
__0.76__

Use with pages 76–77. **23**

Name _____

Another Look 2-13

Analyze Strategies: Draw a Picture

The longest river in the United States that boats can navigate is the Mississippi River. The Yukon River is slightly longer than the Rio Grande, but they are both shorter than the Missouri River. List the rivers from longest to shortest.

What do you know? Lengths of the rivers in comparison to each other

What do you need to find? Lengths of rivers in order

Draw a picture of the four rivers.

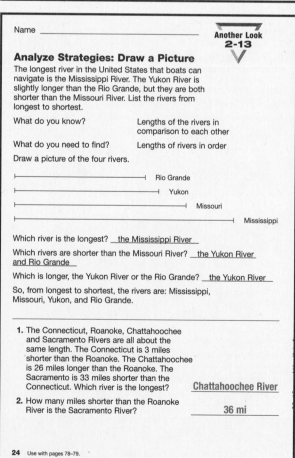

Which river is the longest? __the Mississippi River__

Which rivers are shorter than the Missouri River? __the Yukon River and Rio Grande__

Which is longer, the Yukon River or the Rio Grande? __the Yukon River__

So, from longest to shortest, the rivers are: Mississippi, Missouri, Yukon, and Rio Grande.

1. The Connecticut, Roanoke, Chattahoochee and Sacramento Rivers are all about the same length. The Connecticut is 3 miles shorter than the Roanoke. The Chattahoochee is 26 miles longer than the Roanoke. The Sacramento is 33 miles shorter than the Connecticut. Which river is the longest?   __Chattahoochee River__

2. How many miles shorter than the Roanoke River is the Sacramento River?   __36 mi__

24 Use with pages 78–79.

170

Estimating Sums and Differences

Kenny collects basketball cards. He trades and purchases cards often. Below is a table showing his total collection over four months.

Estimate the number of cards he collected during the fourth month.

You can estimate by rounding.

Step 1 Round numbers to the nearest hundred.

1,071 rounds to 1,100

765 rounds to 800

Month	Total Cards in Collection
1	153
2	459
3	765
4	1,071

Step 2 Add or subtract.

```
  1,100
-   800
    300
```

Kenny collected about __300__ baseball cards during the fourth month.

Estimate each sum or difference.

1.
```
  1,348  rounds to   1,000
+ 2,279  rounds to + 2,000
                     3,000
```

2.
```
   428  rounds to    400
-  171  rounds to  - 200
                     200
```

3.
```
  631
+ 232
  800
```

4.
```
  733
- 532
  200
```

5.
```
  $2.23
+  1.04
  $3.00
```

6.
```
  324
  953
+ 325
1,600
```

7.
```
  1,072
+   614
  1,700
```

8.
```
  683
- 498
  200
```

Adding and Subtracting Whole Numbers

You can use place-value blocks to help you add and subtract.

Add 315 + 126.

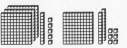

Subtract 341 − 135.

Add the ones.

5 ones + 6 ones = 11 ones
You can exchange 10 ones blocks for 1 tens block.

11 ones = 1 ten __1__ one

Add the tens. Remember you have 1 ten from the ones above.

1 ten + 1 ten + 2 tens = __4__ tens

Add the hundreds.

3 hundreds + 1 hundred = __4__ hundreds

315 + 126 = __441__

Subtract the ones.

You cannot take 5 from 1, so exchange 1 tens block for 10 ones blocks. Now you have 11 ones.

11 ones − 5 ones = __6__ ones

Subtract the tens. Remember you only have 3 tens left.

3 tens − 3 tens = __0__ tens

Subtract the hundreds.

3 hundreds − 1 hundred = __2__ hundreds

341 − 135 = __206__

Add or subtract. Use place-value blocks.

1.
```
  205
+ 127
  332
```

2.
```
  316
- 128
  188
```

Exploring Adding and Subtracting Decimals

In your book you used place-value blocks to add and subtract decimals. Here is another way to add and subtract decimals.

You can use money to show decimals.

```
  3.27
+ 1.35
```

You can exchange 10 of the pennies for another dime.
So, 3.27 + 1.35 = 4.62.

Use place-value blocks or money to find each sum or difference.

1.
```
  3.12
+ 1.29
  4.41
```

2.
```
  4.51
- 1.41
  3.10
```

3.
```
  4.62
+ 1.39
  6.01
```

4.
```
  6.51
+ 2.36
  8.87
```

5.
```
  4.89
- 3.76
  1.13
```

6.
```
  8.91
- 5.02
  3.89
```

Adding Decimals

You can use a string of decimal points to help you add decimals.

To add 4.6, 13 and 0.67, write the numbers so that the decimals are on the string. Write whole numbers to the left of the string. Then add as you add whole numbers.

```
  4.6
 13.
  0.67
 18.27
```

Use the string to add each set of decimals.

1. 3.6, 2.9, and 1.23
```
   3.6
   2.9
+  1.23
   7.73
```

2. 23.7, 0.56, and 5.3
```
  23.7
   0.56
+  5.3
  29.56
```

3. 41.75, 15.1, and 5
```
  41.75
  15.1
+  5.
  61.85
```

4. 0.90, 0.09, and 9.09
```
   0.90
   0.09
+  9.09
  10.08
```

Find each sum.

5. $6.39 + $1.19 = __$7.58__

6. 0.25 + 1.6 + 2.9 = __4.75__

7. 4.29 + 0.06 = __4.35__

8. 6.91 + 11 + 1.2 = __19.11__

9. 3.6 + 0.14 = __3.74__

10. 4.69 + 3.1 + 7 = __14.79__

Subtracting Decimals

You can use place-value blocks to help you subtract decimals.

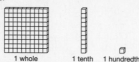

1 whole   1 tenth   1 hundredth

1.25 − 0.16

First subtract the hundredths. Since you cannot take 6 from 5 you must regroup. Regroup 1 tenth as 10 hundredths.

15 hundredths − 6 hundredths = _9_ hundredths

Subtract the tenths.

1 tenth − 1 tenth = _0_ tenths

Subtract the ones.

1 one − 0 ones = _1_ one

$$\begin{array}{r} 1\ 15 \\ 1.\cancel{2}\cancel{5} \\ -0.16 \\ \hline 1.09 \end{array}$$

Use place-value blocks to help you find each difference.

1. 2.35 − 1.41 = _0.94_

2. $\begin{array}{r}6.8\\-1.7\\\hline 5.1\end{array}$	**3.** $\begin{array}{r}2.3\\-0.65\\\hline 1.65\end{array}$	**4.** $\begin{array}{r}6.94\\-0.07\\\hline 6.87\end{array}$	**5.** $\begin{array}{r}8.00\\-1.35\\\hline 6.65\end{array}$

Analyze Word Problems: Choose an Operation

Jan and Bobby went bowling on a Saturday afternoon. Bobby's scores were 98, 134, and 125. Jan's scores were 112, 208, and 99. Who had the greater total score?

What do you know?   You know their scores.

What do you need to find out?   You need to find out whose total score was greater.

Decide what operation makes sense.   Write number sentences to find Bobby's and Jan's total scores. To find a total of two or more numbers, add.

Bobby's scores   98 + 134 + 125 = _357_

Jan's scores   112 + 208 + 99 = _419_

Since _419_ > _357_, Jan's score was greater.

Write a number sentence to solve each problem. Then solve the problem.

1. Marcia and Peter traveled 366 miles on their first day of vacation. The second day they traveled 486 miles. How many miles had they traveled all together?

366 + 486 = 852; 852 miles

2. Karen and Sue run 2 miles every day. Karen has run 486 miles. Sue has run 366 miles. How many more miles has Karen run than Sue?

486 − 366 = 120; 120 miles

3. June read a 576-page book one week and a 328-page book the next. How many pages did she read in all?

579 + 328 = 904; 904 pages

Exploring Multiplication Patterns and Properties

In your book, you explored multiplication patterns and properties. Here is another way to understand properties.

Commutative Property When you commute from home to work by train or car, the distance you go back and forth is the same. The distance stays the same, no matter the order.

$10 \times (2 \times 10) = 10 \times (10 \times 2) = 200$

Associative Property When an association meets members can group themselves in different ways. The association stays the same.

$10 \times (10 \times 2) = (10 \times 10) \times 2 = 200$

You can use properties to make solving $4 \times (7 \times 25)$ easier.

$4 \times (7 \times 25)$ Use the commutative property to change the order. → $4 \times (25 \times 7)$

$4 \times (25 \times 7)$ Use the associative property to change the grouping. → $(4 \times 25) \times 7$

$(4 \times 25) \times 7 = \underline{100 \times 7} = \underline{700}$

Find each product. Use multiplication properties.

1. $(7 \times 5) \times 40 =$
$7 \times (\ \underline{5}\ \times\ \underline{40}\ ) =$
$7 \times \underline{200} = 1{,}400$

2. $100 \times (30 \times 7) =$
$(100 \times \underline{30}\ ) \times \underline{7} =$
$\underline{3{,}000} \times 7 = 21{,}000$

3. $8 \times (10 \times 3) = \underline{240}$

4. $30 \times (40 \times 5) = \underline{6{,}000}$

5. $50 \times (4 \times 2) = \underline{400}$

6. $(8 \times 70) \times 10 = \underline{5{,}600}$

Estimating Products

To estimate a product, you can round before you multiply. Look at these two examples.

	Round	Use Mental Math	Estimate
398 × 18	400 × 20	4 × 2 = 8	8,000
398 × 99	400 × 100	4 × 1 = 4	40,000

Estimate the product. Round. Then use mental math.

1. 7 × 37
$7 \times 40 = \underline{280}$

2. 8 × 74
$8 \times 70 = \underline{560}$

3. 89 × 6
$\underline{90} \times 6 = \underline{540}$

4. 63 × 170
$\underline{60} \times 200 = \underline{12{,}000}$

5. 22 × 99
$\underline{20} \times 100 = \underline{2{,}000}$

6. 38 × 41
$40 \times \underline{40} = \underline{1{,}600}$

7. 59 × 78
$\underline{60} \times \underline{80} = \underline{4{,}800}$

8. 198 × 61
$\underline{200} \times \underline{60} = \underline{12{,}000}$

9. 33 × 34
$\underline{30} \times \underline{30} = \underline{900}$

10. 102 × 48
$\underline{100} \times \underline{50} = \underline{5{,}000}$

Multiplying Whole Numbers

Find the product: 56 × 23

You can use place value to help you multiply whole numbers. Break up whole numbers to make them easier to multiply mentally. Pair the pieces of each number and multiply.

56 = 50 + 6   50 + 6   50 + 6
23 = 20 + 3   × 20 + 3   × 20 + 3

3 × 6 = 18   20 × 6 = 120
3 × 50 = 150   20 × 50 = 1,000

Find the sum of all the partial products.

120 + 18 + 1,000 + 150 = __1,288__

56 × 23 = __1,288__

Complete each problem.

1. 28 × 87

a. 28 = 20 + 8   20 + 8
   87 = 80 + 7   × 80 + 7

7 × 8 = __56__   80 × 8 = __640__
7 × __20__ = 140 80 × __20__ = 1,600

b. Find the sum of all the partial products. __2,436__

c. 28 × 87 = __2,436__

2. 37	**3.** 59	**4.** 438	**5.** 85
×42	×23	× 63	×53
1,554	1,357	27,594	4,505

Distributive Property

The distributive property lets you break up numbers before you multiply.

To multiply 2 × 126, break 126 into 120 + 6.

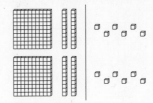

2 × 126 = 2 × (120 + 6)
     = (2 × 120) + (2 × 6)
     =   240 + 12
     = __252__

Complete each problem.

1. 3 × 18 = 3 × (__10__ + __8__)
    = (3 × __10__) + (3 × __8__)
    = __30__ + __24__
    = __54__

2. 253 × 4 = 4 × (__250__ + __3__)
    = (4 × __250__) + (4 × __3__)
    = __1,000__ + __12__
    = __1,012__

3. 404 × 2 = 2 × (__400__ + __4__)
    = (__2__ × 400) + (2 × __4__)
    = __800__ + 8
    = __808__

4. 8 × 128 = 8 × (__800__ + __800__)
    = (__8__ × __120__) + (8 × 8)
    = 960 + __64__
    = __1,024__

Choosing a Calculation Method

Using different calculation methods for different problems will save you time. Before you multiply, think about which method is best for each problem.

Use mental math

- for problems with zeros   400 × 50
- for problems with numbers
  near benchmarks   199 × 20
- for short problems   22 × 7
- for easy problems   15 × 6

Use a calculator

- for problems with large numbers 928,640 × 741,306
- for difficult problems   84,996 × 5,588
- when you want the exact answer quickly 14 × 15

Use paper and pencil   735

- the rest of the time   × 26

What method would you use to solve each problem? Circle one. Then solve, using that method.

Possible answers:

1. 302 × 84 = __25,368__
    mental math
    calculator
    (paper and pencil)

2. 74 × 20 = __1,480__
    (mental math)
    calculator
    paper and pencil

3. 67,989
  × 787
  53,507,343
    mental math
    (calculator)
    paper and pencil

Exploring Patterns with Multiples

In your book you used patterns to explore multiples. Here is another way to explore multiples. On this grid, multiples of 2 are shaded and multiples of 3 are crossed.

1	2	3	4	5	6	7	8	9	10
11	12	13	14	15	16	17	18	19	20

Common multiples are multiples that are shared by two or more numbers. The common multiples of 2 and 3 are 6, 12, and 18. Each common multiple of 2 and 3 is circled on the grid above. The least common multiple (LCM) of 2 and 3 is 6.

Use this grid to help you answer **1–4.**

1	2	3	4	5	6	7	8	9	10
11	12	13	14	15	16	17	18	19	20
21	22	23	24	25	26	27	28	29	30
31	32	33	34	35	36	37	38	39	40

1. Shade the multiples of 4.   **2.** Cross the multiples of 5.

3. What are the common multiples of 4 and 5 on the grid? __20, 40__

4. What is the least common multiple of 4 and 5 on the grid? __20__

Use this grid to help you answer **5–8.**

1	2	3	4	5	6	7	8	9	10
11	12	13	14	15	16	17	18	19	20
21	22	23	24	25	26	27	28	29	30
31	32	33	34	35	36	37	38	39	40
41	42	43	44	45	46	47	48	49	50
51	52	53	54	55	56	57	58	59	60

5. Shade the multiples of 6.   **6.** Cross the multiples of 8.

7. What are the common multiples of 6 and 8? __24, 48__

8. What is the least common multiple of 6 and 8? __24__

Decision Making

Sanur is buying dinner for himself and two friends. Jane wants salad, juice, and a veggie burger. Chas wants juice and a hamburger but no salad. Sanur wants salad and a hamburger, but a different kind of juice than Jane and Chas.

Menu			
	Small (Serves 1)	Medium (Serves 2)	Large (Serves 3)
Hamburger	$3.00		
Veggie Burger	$3.50		
Salad	$1.00		$2.50
Juice	$0.75	$1.25	$1.50

1. Who can share juice? Chas and Jane

2. Will anyone share salad? No, only two people want salad, so a large salad would be too big.

3. What will Sanur buy? 2 hamburgers, 1 veggie burger, 2 small salads, 1 small juice and 1 medium juice

4. How much will it cost? Show the cost of each item.*
   $(2 \times \$3.00) + \$3.50 + (2 \times \$1.00) + \$0.75 + \$1.25 = \$13.50$

5. If everyone wanted a hamburger, salad, and the same juice, what would Sanur buy?
   3 hamburgers, 1 large salad, and 1 large juice

6. How much would this cost? Show the cost of each item.
   $(3 \times \$3.00) + \$2.50 + \$1.50 = \$13.00$

7. What is the difference between the two costs?
   $0.50

Exploring Decimal Patterns

In your book, you used a calculator to explore patterns.

You can use place-value patterns to find the product of a decimal and a power of ten. Whole numbers that end in 0 are a power of ten.

Find 2.5 × 100.

Which number is a power of 10? __100__

To multiply a decimal by a power of ten, count the number of zeros at the end of the power of ten. How many are there? _2_

Move the decimal point over that same number of places, adding a zero if necessary.

$2.5 \times 100 = 2.5 = 2.50 = $ __250__

Find each product.

1. 3.4 × 1,000
   a. Which number is a power of ten? __1,000__
   b. How many zeros are in that power of ten? __3 zeros__
   c. How many places should you move the decimal point to find the product? __3 places__
   d. Write the product. __3,400__

2. 5.2 × 100 = __520__
3. 4.7 × 1,000 = __4,700__
4. 3.83 × 10 = __38.3__
5. 1.76 × 1,000 = __1,760__
6. 4.52 × 100 = __452__
7. 8.6 × 1,000 = __8,600__
8. 9.103 × 100 = __91.03__
9. 5.387 × 1,000 = __5,387__
10. 1.54 × 100 = __154__
11. 3.265 × 1,000 = __3,265__
12. 0.25 × 100 = __25__
13. 0.700 × 1,000 = __700__
14. 0.1 × 100 = __10__
15. 2.43 × 1,000 = __2,430__
16. Find the product of 6.0253 and 1,000. __6,025.3__

Estimating Decimal Products

You can use a number line to estimate products.

Estimate 28 × 7.36.

First round 28 to the nearest ten.

Look at the digit right of the tens digit. 2<u>8</u>

28 rounds to 30 because 8 is greater than 5.

On the number line you can see that 28 is closer to 30 than to 20.

Round 7.36 to the nearest one.

Look at the digit right of the ones digit. 7.<u>3</u>6

7.36 rounds to 7 because 3 is less than 5.

On the number line you can see that 7.36 is closer to 7 than to 8.

Multiply the rounded numbers to find the estimate of the product.
30 × 7 = __210__

The estimated product of 28 and 7.36 is __210__.

Estimate each product.

1. 4.3 × 31
   a. Round 31 to the nearest ten. __30__
   b. Round 4.3 to the nearest one. __4__
   c. Find the product of the rounded numbers. __120__

2. 4.85 × 23 __100__
3. 48 × 3.16 __150__
4. 97.8 × 59 __600__
4. 3.6 × 47 __200__
5. 67.7 × 49 __3,500__
6. 2.6 × 26 __90__

Multiplying Whole Numbers and Decimals

You can use place-value blocks to help you to multiply decimals.

2.43 × 3

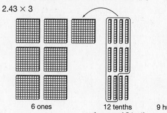

| 6 ones | 12 tenths or 1 one and 2 tenths | 9 hundredths |

Count the blocks in each place. Regroup when necessary.

2.43 × 3 = 7.29

Find each product. You can draw place-value blocks to help.

1. 3.13 × 4 = __12.52__
2. 3 × 1.25 = __3.75__

3. 16.95 × 5 = __84.75__
4. 20 × 4.03 = __80.6__
5. 7.49 × 27 = __202.23__
6. 6 × 8.51 = __51.06__
7. 18 × 1.45 = __26.10__
8. 17.11 × 5 = __85.55__
9. 4.72 × 39 = __184.08__
10. 7 × 2.24 = __15.68__
11. 7 × 10.36 = __72.52__
12. 5.06 × 9 = __45.54__
13. 12 × 12.04 = __144.48__
14. 6.43 × 11 = __70.73__

Analyzing Word Problems: Multiple-Step Problems

Nadia is planning to grow tomatoes. She needs 2 packs of seeds and 2 stakes. Packs of tomato seeds are $1.19 each and stakes are $0.50 each. What will be the total cost of her garden project?

Understand

What question do you need to answer?

How much will 2 packs of seeds and 2 stakes cost.

Plan

What is the cost of 1 pack of tomato seeds? $1.19

How much will 1 stake cost? $0.50

Solve

Step 1 Find the cost of 2 packs of seeds. $2 \times \$1.19 = \$2.38$

Step 2 Find the cost of 2 stakes. $2 \times \$0.50 = \$1.00$

Step 3 Find the total. $\$2.38 + \$1.00 = \$3.38$

Solve each problem.

1. Nadia plants 6 large tomato plants and 5 cherry tomato plants. There are 12 tomatoes on each large tomato plant and 22 tomatoes on each cherry tomato plant. How many tomatoes does she have in all?   **182 tomatoes**

2. Nadia sold 66 of her large tomatoes for $0.50 each and 100 of her cherry tomatoes for $0.05 each.

   a. How much money did she earn? $38.00

   b. How many tomatoes does she have left?   66

3. Next time Nadia grows tomatoes, she plans on buying plant food, which costs $4.29 a pack. If she buys 3 packs and a watering can for $3.79, how much will she spend?   _$16.66_

Exploring Decimal Multiplication

In your book, you used grids to find decimal products. Here is another way to multiply decimals.

Find 0.3 of 0.5.

Make an array using dimes and pennies.

Make one row of 3 dimes and one column of 5 dimes.

Make an array of pennies next to the dimes.

Count the pennies. Write the amount using a decimal.

0.3 of 0.5 is _0.15_.

Use dimes and pennies to help you find each product.

1. 0.8 of 0.3

   a. Draw pennies to complete the array.

   b. How many pennies are there?   _24_

   c. 0.8 of 0.3 is _0.24_.

2. 0.4 of 0.5

   a. How many dimes will you need?   9

   b. How many pennies are in the array?   20

   c. 0.4 of 0.5 is _0.20_.

3. 0.3 of 0.7 is _0.21_.   4. 0.2 of 0.8 is _0.16_.

5. 0.4 of 0.4 is _0.16_.   6. 0.9 of 0.3 is _0.27_.

Multiplying Decimals by Decimals

For each product, write the decimal point in the correct place.

$3.45 \times 2.5 = 8625$

Find the number of decimal places in the factors. 3.45×2.3

_2_ decimal places + _1_ decimal place = _3_ decimal places

Place the decimal point in the product 3 decimal places from the right.

$3.45 \times 2.5 =$ _8.625_

Follow the same steps to write the decimal point in the correct place for each product.

1. 21.6×0.8

   a. _1_ decimal place(s) + _1_ decimal place(s) = _2_ decimal places

   b. $21.6 \times 0.8 = 1728$ **17.28**

2. 0.04×8

   a. _2_ decimal places + _0_ decimal places = _2_ decimal places

   b. $0.04 \times 8 = 32$ **0.32**

3. $\begin{array}{r} 5.08 \\ \times\ 0.4 \\ \hline 2.032 \end{array}$ 4. $\begin{array}{r} 70.5 \\ \times\ 0.02 \\ \hline 1.41 \end{array}$ 5. $\begin{array}{r} 1.342 \\ \times\ 2.7 \\ \hline 3.6234 \end{array}$ 6. $\begin{array}{r} 9.08 \\ \times\ 0.04 \\ \hline 0.3632 \end{array}$

7. $\begin{array}{r} 6.53 \\ \times\ 1.9 \\ \hline 12.407 \end{array}$ 8. $\begin{array}{r} 7.48 \\ \times\ 1.03 \\ \hline 7.7044 \end{array}$ 9. $\begin{array}{r} 8.87 \\ \times\ 0.5 \\ \hline 4.435 \end{array}$ 10. $\begin{array}{r} 2.235 \\ \times\ 1.7 \\ \hline 3.7995 \end{array}$

11. Check your answer to 4. Explain why it is different from the others?

    Possible answer: Because there is an "invisible" zero at the

    end, it looks like the decimal point is positioned incorrectly.

Finding High and Low Estimates

You can use high and low estimates to find the range of a product before multiplying.

85.79×3.3 **A.** 110 and 240   **B.** 255 and 280   **C.** 240 and 360

Between which two numbers will the product be found?

For a low estimate, use the first digit of each number. Change remaining digits to 0.

$80 \times 3 =$ _240_ Low Estimate

For a high estimate, increase the first digit by 1. Change remaining digits to 0.

$90 \times 4 =$ _360_ High Estimate

The range for 85.79×3.3 is _240_ to _360_.

The product will be found between 240 and 360.

Between which two numbers will each product be found?

1. 3.2×7.79 **A.** 37 and 73   **B.** 10 and 21   **C.** 21 and 32

   Low estimate: _21_   High Estimate: _32_   Answer: _C_

2. 8.93×9.7 **A.** 17 and 79   **B.** 72 and 90   **C.** 93 and 97

   Low estimate: _72_   High Estimate: _90_   Answer: _B_

3. 6.73×71.2 **A.** 420 and 560   **B.** 240 and 650   **C.** 130 and 240

   Low estimate: _420_   High Estimate: _560_   Answer: _A_

4. 4.7×6.94 **A.** 12 and 16   **B.** 24 and 35   **C.** 24 and 30

   Low estimate: _24_   High Estimate: _35_   Answer: _B_

5. 12.3×4.8 **A.** 48 and 52   **B.** 16 and 48   **C.** 40 and 100

   Low estimate: _40_   High Estimate: _100_   Answer: _C_

Name _____

Another Look
3-15

Decimals and Zeros

Multiplying decimals is similar to multiplying whole numbers. The only difference is placing the decimal point.

0.6×0.002

Step 1   Count the decimal places.

0.6	0.002	product
1 number after the decimal point	+ 3 numbers after the decimal point	= 4 numbers after the decimal point

Step 2   Multiply as with whole numbers. Add zeros to the left of the product to give enough digits before the decimal point.

$6 \times 2 = 12$

$0.6 \times 0.002 = \underline{0.0012}$

Find each product.

1. 0.08×0.006

   a.

0.08	0.006	product
$\underline{2}$ numbers after the decimal point	+ $\underline{3}$ numbers after the decimal point	= $\underline{5}$ numbers after the decimal point

   b. $8 \times 6 = \underline{48}$

   c. $0.08 \times 0.006 = \underline{0.00048}$

2. 0.0 7 × 0.7 ‾‾‾‾‾ 0.049	**3.** 1.6 × 0.0 0 2 ‾‾‾‾‾ 0.0032	**4.** 0.0 1 × 0.0 1 ‾‾‾‾‾ 0.0001	**5.** 0.0 5 × 0.0 2 ‾‾‾‾‾ 0.001

6. Check your answer to question **5.** Does it follow the rule? Why or why not?

Possible answer: Yes; because $2 \times 5 = 10$, the answer could be written as 0.0010.

Use with pages 154–155.   **45**

Name _____

Another Look
3-16

Analyzing Strategies: Guess and Check

A store manager is planning a 100-hour work schedule for the week. The manager schedules 6-hour and 8-hour long shifts. There will be two more 8-hour shifts than 6-hour shifts. How many shifts for each time period will there be?

You know that there are 6-hour and 8-hour shifts. Altogether the shifts must total 100 hours.

Make a guess for the number of 6-hour shifts. You know there will be 2 more 8-hour shifts.

	6-hour shifts	8-hour shifts	Total hours
Guess 1:	2	4	$(2 \times 6) + (4 \times 8) = 44$–too low
Guess 2:	8	10	$(8 \times 6) + (10 \times 8) = 128$–too high
Guess 3:	5	$\underline{7}$	$(5 \times 6) + (\underline{7} \times 8) = \underline{86}$ –too low
Guess 4:	6	$\underline{8}$	$(6 \times 6) + (\underline{8} \times 8) + \underline{100}$.

The first guess is too low. Try a greater number for your second guess.

The second guess is too high. Your next guess should be between two and eight 6-hour shifts.

The schedule will have __6__ 6-hour shifts and __8__ 8-hour shifts.

1. Together, Stephanie and Jane have saved $65.50 towards buying a new telescope. Jane has saved $9.50 more than Stephanie. How much did each contribute? Use the table to help you organize your guesses.

	Stephanie's Contribution	Jane's Contribution	Total
Guess 1:	$10.00	$\underline{\$19.50}$	$10.00 + $\underline{\$19.50}$ = $\underline{\$29.50}$
Guess 2:	$30.00	$\underline{\$39.50}$	$30.00 + $\underline{\$39.50}$ = $\underline{\$69.50}$
Guess 3:			
Guess 4:	$28.00	$37.50	$28.00 + $37.50 = $65.50

Stephanie contributed $ __28.00__ and Jane contributed $ __37.50__ .

46   Use with pages 156–157.

Name _____

Another Look
4-1

Reviewing the Meaning of Division

You can use counters to help you divide.

Find $20 \div 4$.

Place 20 counters on your desk.

You have 20 counters. You need to divide them into groups of 4.

How many groups of 4 are there? __5__

So, $20 \div 4 = 5$.

Find each quotient. Use counters to help.

1. $24 \div 8$

   a. Draw counters in the space to the right to show 24 counters divided into groups of 8.

   b. How many groups of 8 counters are there? __3__

   c. $24 \div 8 = $ __3__

2. $15 \div 3 = $ __5__   **3.** $42 \div 6 = $ __7__

4. $36 \div 9 = $ __4__   **5.** $64 \div 8 = $ __8__

6. $12 \div 2 = $ __6__   **7.** $21 \div 7 = $ __3__

Use with pages 168–169.   **47**

Name _____

Another Look
4-2

Exploring Patterns to Divide

In your book you used a calculator to find division patterns. Here is another way to use patterns to divide.

Use the basic fact $12 \div 2 = 6$ to help you divide larger numbers.

12 tens ÷ 2 = 6 tens

$120 \div 2 = 60$ There is one zero in the dividend and no zeros in the divisor. Place one zero in the quotient.

12 hundreds ÷ 2 = 6 hundreds

$1,200 \div 2 = 600$ There are two zeros in the dividend and no zeros in the divisor. Place two zeros in the quotient.

12 thousands ÷ 2 = 6 thousands

$12,000 \div 2 = 6,000$ There are three zeros in the dividend and no zeros in the divisor. Place three zeros in the quotient.

You can use basic facts and patterns to divide larger numbers.

Use patterns and basic facts to divide.

1. $36,000 \div 4$

   a. Basic fact: $36 \div 4 = $ __9__

   b. Add one zero to the end of the quotient: $360 \div 4 = $ __90__

   c. Add two zeros to the end of the quotient: $3,600 \div 4 = $ __900__

   d. $36,000 \div 4 = $ __9,000__

2. $1,800 \div 6$

   a. What basic fact will you use to help find the answer? $18 \div 6 = 3$

   b. $1,800 \div 6 = $ __300__

3. $250 \div 5 = $ __50__   **4.** $1,400 \div 7 = $ __200__

48   Use with pages 170–171.

176

Name _____

Estimating Quotients

Estimate 172 ÷ 3.

To estimate a quotient, just look at the first two digits of
the dividend. Think: 15 ÷ 3 = 5, so 17 ÷ 3 is close to 5 and
170 ÷ 3 is close to 50.

Since 170 ÷ 3 is about 50, a good estimate for 172 ÷ 3
is about 50.

Estimate.

1. 316 ÷ 5
   a. 31 ÷ 5 is about __6__.
   b. How many zeros should you add to the quotient? __1__
   c. A reasonable estimate for 316 ÷ 5 is __60__.

2. 436 ÷ 8
   a. __43__ ÷ 8 is about __5__.
   b. How many zeros should you add to the quotient? __1__
   c. A reasonable estimate for 436 ÷ 8 is __50__.

3. 297 ÷ 4
   a. __29__ ÷ 4 is about __7__.
   b. 297 ÷ 4 is about __70__

4. 655 ÷ 7
   a. __65__ ÷ 7 is about __9__.
   b. 655 ÷ 7 is about __90__

5. 195 ÷ 6 __30__   6. 237 ÷ 7 __30__

7. 509 ÷ 9 __50 or 60__   8. 714 ÷ 8 __90__

Name _____

Exploring Dividing

In your book you used play money to solve division
problems. Here is another way to divide money.

Divide $4.28 by 3.

Divide the dollars by repeated
subtraction. How many groups
of 3 dollars can you take away? __1__

Change any dollars that
are left to dimes.

Divide the dimes by repeated
subtraction. How many groups
of 3 dimes can you take away? __4__

Change any dimes that are left to pennies.

Divide the pennies by repeated
subtraction. How many groups
of 3 pennies can you take away? __2__

How many pennies are left over? __2__

Write the quotient using a dollar sign and a decimal point.

$4.28 ÷ 3 = 1 group of dollars, 4 groups of dimes, 2 groups
of pennies, and 2 pennies left over.

$4.28 ÷ 3 = $1.42 R2

Find the quotient.
$6.16 ÷ 5
   1. How many groups of 5 dollars can you make? __1__
   2. How many groups of 5 dimes can you make? __2__
   3. How many groups of 5 pennies can you make? __3__
   4. How many pennies are left over? __1__
   5. Write the quotient. __$1.23 R1__

Name _____

Dividing by 1-Digit Divisors

4)257

You can use place-value blocks to divide.

Step 1 Use place-value blocks to show 257.

Step 2 Since you cannot divide the hundreds blocks into four equal groups, regroup the hundreds as tens.

Step 3 Divide the tens into four equal groups.

Step 4 Regroup the left over tens as ones.

Step 5 Divide the ones into four equal groups.

Step 6 Find the number in one group.
    6 tens + 4 ones = 60 + 4 = 64   64 R1
                                      4)257

Use place-value blocks to divide.

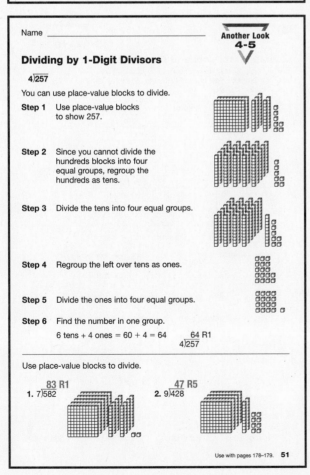

1. 83 R1 / 7)582   2. 47 R5 / 9)428

Name _____

Analyze Word Problems: Interpret Remainders

Tia went to the book closet to get notebooks for her class of
32 students. The notebooks are packed 6 to a carton. How
many cartons does she need?

You know that each carton holds
6 notebooks. Tia needs to get
enough cartons for 32 students.

You can draw a picture to help
you solve the problem. Each
carton represents 6 notebooks.

Are 5 cartons enough? 5 × 6 = 30   5 R2 / 6)32 / −30 / 2
No, 2 more notebooks are needed.

Are 6 cartons enough? 6 × 6 = 36 __Yes__.

In the lunchroom, students sit at tables of 6. There are 82
students eating lunch. How many tables must be set up?

1. How many students sit at 1 table? __6 students__
2. Draw a picture to show the number of tables needed.
3. How many tables are needed? __14 tables__
4. How many of the tables will be full? __13 tables__
5. At the right, show the division problem
   you could use to solve the problem.

13 R4 / 6)82 / −6 / 22 / −18 / 4

177

Deciding Where to Place the First Digit

When you divide, how do you find where to place the first digit of your quotient? You can estimate the answer or you can try the following approach.

Look at the first digit of the dividend. Is it equal to or greater than the divisor? If so, begin writing your answer above the first digit of the dividend. $\overset{123}{3\overline{)369}}$
If the first digit of the dividend is less than the divisor, begin writing your answer above the 2nd digit of the dividend. $\overset{89}{3\overline{)267}}$

Decide where to place the first digit of your answer. Then solve the problem.

$$\overset{214}{2\overline{)428}}$$

Where does the quotient's first digit go? Explain.

  In the hundreds place because the 4 in 428 is greater than the divisor.

1. $4\overline{)484}$

   a. Where does the quotient's first digit go? Explain.

      in the hundreds place; because the 4 in 484 is equal to

      the divisor

   b. Find the quotient. __121__

2. $6\overline{)372}$

   a. Where does the quotient's first digit go? Explain.

      in the tens place; because the 3 in 372 is less than

      the divisor

   b. Find the quotient. __62__

Zeros in the Quotient

$3\overline{)626}$

You can use place-value blocks to show division.

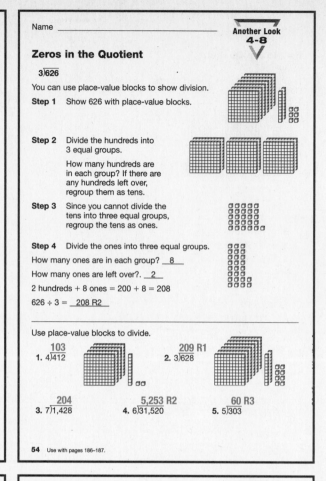

Step 1 Show 626 with place-value blocks.

Step 2 Divide the hundreds into 3 equal groups.

How many hundreds are in each group? If there are any hundreds left over, regroup them as tens.

Step 3 Since you cannot divide the tens into three equal groups, regroup the tens as ones.

Step 4 Divide the ones into three equal groups.

How many ones are in each group? __8__

How many ones are left over?. __2__

2 hundreds + 8 ones = 200 + 8 = 208

626 ÷ 3 = __208 R2__

Use place-value blocks to divide.

1. $\overset{103}{4\overline{)412}}$

2. $\overset{209\ R1}{3\overline{)628}}$

3. $\overset{204}{7\overline{)1,428}}$

4. $\overset{5,253\ R2}{6\overline{)31,520}}$

5. $\overset{60\ R3}{5\overline{)303}}$

Exploring Mean

In your book you used estimates to explore mean. Here is another way to understand the mean.

Find the mean, median, and mode for this set of data.

7, 7, 10, 11, 7, 6, 8

Step 1 Order the numbers from least to greatest.

Step 2 To find the **mean**, find the sum of the numbers. Then divide by the number of addends. There are 7 addends, so divide by 7.
56 ÷ 7 = 8
The mean is __8__.

Step 3 To find the **median**, find the number in the exact middle of the list. There are 3 numbers on either side of 7, so the median is __7__.

Step 4 To find the **mode**, look for the number that occurs most often. Since there are three 7s, the mode is __7__.

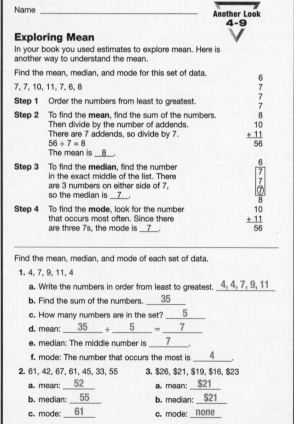

Find the mean, median, and mode of each set of data.

1. 4, 7, 9, 11, 4

   a. Write the numbers in order from least to greatest. __4, 4, 7, 9, 11__

   b. Find the sum of the numbers. __35__

   c. How many numbers are in the set? __5__

   d. mean: __35__ ÷ __5__ = __7__

   e. median: The middle number is __7__.

   f. mode: The number that occurs the most is __4__.

2. 61, 42, 67, 61, 45, 33, 55

   a. mean: __52__

   b. median: __55__

   c. mode: __61__

3. $26, $21, $19, $16, $23

   a. mean: __$21__

   b. median: __$21__

   c. mode: __none__

Exploring Products and Quotients

In your book you explored products and quotients by testing examples. Here is another way to remember facts about products and quotients.

Factor	Factor	Product
n	1	n
> 1	> 1	> either factor
n	0	0

Dividend	Divisor	Quotient
n	1	n
> 1	> 1	< dividend
0	n	0

Look for clues in the factors. Complete using >, <, or =.

1.
   4 8 → factor is (>) 1
   × 5 → factor is (>) 1
   product is (>) either factor

2.
   4 9 8 → factor is (>) 1
   × 1 → factor is (=) 1
   product is (=) the first factor

3.
   9 2 7 → factor is (>) 1
   × 0 → factor is (=) 0
   product is (=) 0

4.
   7 9 → factor is (>) 1
   × 8 → factor is (>) 1
   product is (>) either factor

5. $1\overline{)1,267}$

   The dividend is (>) 1.

   The divisor is (=) 1.

   The quotient is (=) the dividend.

6. $56\overline{)475}$

   The dividend is (>) 1.

   The divisor is (>) 1.

   The quotient is (<) the dividend.

Another Look
4-11

Dividing Money

You can divide money in the same way that you divide whole numbers.

To divide $73.26 by 3, first find 7,326 ÷ 3.

Divide the thousands. Multiply, subtract, and compare.

Divide the hundreds. Multiply, subtract, and compare.

Divide the tens. Multiply, subtract, and compare.

Divide the ones. Multiply, subtract, and compare.

```
    2,442
3)7,326
   -6
    13
   -12
    12
   -12
    06
    -6
     0
```

Write the dollar sign and decimal point in the answer. The decimal point goes in front of the tens digit.

$73.26 ÷ 3 = __$24.42__

Find each quotient.

1. 5)$76.15

   a. Write the whole number division problem you can solve to help you find the quotient.

   7,615 ÷ 5

   b. Find the whole number quotient.

   1,523

   c. Find the money quotient.

   $15.23

2. 4)$65.32 $16.33

3. 3)$34.41 $11.47

Another Look
4-12

Dividing Decimals

You can use place-value blocks to help you divide decimals.

Find the quotient. 4)6.12

Divide the ones. How many groups of 4 ones can you make? __1__ Exchange each of the remaining ones for 10 tenths.

Divide the tenths. How many groups of 4 tenths can you make? __5__ Exchange each of the remaining tenths for 10 hundredths.

Divide the hundredths. How many groups of 4 hundredths can you make? __3__

Count the number of groups of each block you have and write the quotient.

1 group of ones, 5 groups of tenths, and 3 groups of hundredths
1 + 0.5 + 0.03 = 1.53

6.12 ÷ 4 = __1.53__

Find each quotient. Use place-value blocks to help.

1. 5)8.85   1.77

2. 3)13.2   4.4

3. 6)17.52   2.92

Another Look
4-13

Factors and Divisibility

A factor evenly divides a given number.

You can use multiplication facts to help you find factors.

Find the factors of 18.

Look for whole numbers whose product is 18.

Start with 1.

1 × 18 = 18	**1** and **18** are factors of 18.
2 × 9 = 18	**2** and **9** are factors of 18.
3 × 6 = 18	**3** and **6** are factors of 18.
4 × ? = 18	There are no numbers that will give a product
5 × ? = 18	of 18 when multiplied by 4 or 5.

All the factors of 18 have been found since the factors greater than 4 and 5 are also shown in the number sentences above.

The factors of 18 are __1, 2, 3, 6, 9, and 18__.

Find the factors for each number. Write multiplication facts to show the factors.

1. 24

   a. 1 × __24__ = 24

   b. 2 × __12__ = 24

   c. 3 × __8__ = 24

   d. 4 × __6__ = 24

   e. List all the factors of 24. __1, 2, 3, 4, 6, 8, 12, 24__

2. 15

   a. Write all the multiplication facts that show the factors of 15.

   1 × 15 = 15, 3 × 5 = 15

   b. List all the factors of 15. __1, 3, 5, 15__

Another Look
4-14

Exploring Prime and Composite Numbers

In your book you used a hundred chart to find prime and composite numbers. Here is another way to find prime and composite numbers.

A **composite number** has more than two factors. Using counters, you can make a rectangle with more than one row.

6 is a composite number.
Its factors are __1, 2, 3, and 6__.

A **prime number** has only two factors. Using counters, you cannot make a rectangle with more than one row.

7 is a prime number.
Its factors are __1 and 7__.

1. a. Form a rectangle with 21 counters.

   b. Is 21 prime or composite? __composite__

2. a. Form a rectangle with 23 counters.

   b. Is 23 prime or composite? __prime__

3. a. Form a rectangle with 35 counters.

   b. Is 35 prime or composite? __composite__

Write whether each number is prime or composite.

4. 18   5. 29   6. 45

__composite__   __prime__   __composite__

Name _____

Another Look
4-15

Analyze Strategies: Work Backward

Two hours after opening, Mr. Irving's newsstand sold 18 newspapers. Half of the remaining newspapers were sold before closing. There were 10 newspapers left. How many newspapers were at the newsstand when it opened?

You can work backward from the end to the beginning. Undo each step.

Ending	Multiply by 2	Add 18	Starting
10	$10 \times 2 = 20$	$20 + 18 = 38$	38

$10 \times 2 = 20$, $20 + 18 = 38$

So, there were __38 newspapers__ at the store when it opened.

Work backward to solve each problem. Complete each drawing to show the steps.

1. Lucia finished her chores at 5:00 P.M. She spent 15 minutes cleaning her room and three times that amount of time washing the dishes. At what time did Lucia start her chores? __4:00 P.M.__

Ending		Cleaning Room		Washing Dishes		Starting
5:00 P.M.	→	− 15 min	→	− 45 min	→	4:00 P.M.

2. Mrs. Oakley bought day-old bread from a bakery for $0.50. The bread had been marked down twice — $\frac{1}{2}$ off the first time, and $\frac{1}{2}$ off the second time. What was the original price of the bread?
__$2.00__

Ending		$\frac{1}{2}$ off		$\frac{1}{2}$ off		Starting
$0. 50	→	× 2	→	× 2	→	$2.00

Use with pages 208–211. **61**

Name _____

Another Look
5-1

Exploring Division Patterns

In your book you used a calculator to explore division patterns. Here is another way to understand division patterns. You can use basic facts to help you divide.

Example 1

Use the basic fact $18 \div 9 = 2$ to help you divide.

$18,000 \div 9 = 2,000$
$18,000 \div 90 = 200$
$18,000 \div 900 = 20$

What pattern do you see? __As the divisor increases by a multiple of 10, the quotient decreases by a multiple of 10.__

Example 2

Use the basic fact $15 \div 3 = 5$ to help you divide.

$15 \div 3 = 5$
$150 \div 3 = 50$
$1,500 \div 3 = 500$

What pattern do you see? __As the dividend increases by a multiple of 10, the quotient increases by a multiple of 10.__

Find each quotient. Use basic facts and patterns to help.

1. $24,000 \div 40$

  a. What basic fact will you use to help solve the problem? __$24 \div 4 = 6$__

  b. What is the quotient of $24,000 \div 4$? __6,000__

  c. $24,000 \div 40 = $ __600__

2. $2,700 \div 9$

  a. What basic fact will you use to help solve the problem? __$27 \div 9 = 3$__

  b. $2,700 \div 9 = $ __300__

3. $12,000 \div 300 = $ __40__   **4.** $1,400 \div 70 = $ __20__

5. $16,000 \div 20 = $ __800__   **6.** $28,000 \div 4 = $ __7,000__

62 Use with pages 222–223.

Name _____

Another Look
5-2

Estimating Quotients: High and Low

You can use basic facts to estimate quotients.

Estimate the quotient of $13,145 \div 50$. Give a high and low estimate.

Think $13 \div 5$.

What two basic facts could help you estimate?

$13 \div 5$ is close to the basic facts $10 \div 5 = 2$ and $15 \div 5 = 3$.

$10 \div 5 = 2$ $15 \div 5 = 3$
$10,000 \div 50 = 200$ $15,000 \div 50 = 300$
The low estimate is __200__.   The high estimate is __300__.

The exact quotient is __between 200 and 300__.

Estimate each quotient. Give a high and low estimate.

1. $23,093 \div 30$ Possible estimates are shown

  a. Name two basic facts that are close to $23 \div 3$. __$24 \div 3 = 8, 21 \div 3 = 7$__

  b. Write the number sentences you will use to find the estimates.
  __$24,000 \div 30 = 800; 21,000 \div 30 = 700$__

2. $3,427 \div 60$

  a. Name two basic facts that are close to $34 \div 6$. __$36 \div 6 = 6; 30 \div 6 = 5$__

  b. Write the number sentences you will use to find the estimates.
  __$3,600 \div 60 = 60; 3,000 \div 60 = 50$__

3. $4,089 \div 70$ __60, 50__   **4.** $35,274 \div 40$ __900, 800__

5. $8,127 \div 90$ __100, 90__   **6.** $17,056 \div 80$ __300, 200__

7. $4,388 \div 70$ __70, 60__   **8.** $23,544 \div 70$ __400, 300__

Use with pages 224–225. **63**

Name _____

Another Look
5-3

Estimating with 2-Digit Divisors

You can use basic facts and compatible numbers to estimate with 2-digit divisors.

Estimate the $423 \div 21$.

Think about basic facts that could help you estimate. (Hint: Look at the front digits of each number to help!)

$4 \div 2 = 2$

$400 \div 20 = 20$

$423 \div 21$ is about 20.

Use basic facts to estimate each quotient.

1. $898 \div 32$

  a. What basic fact could you use to estimate the quotient? __$9 \div 3 = 3$__

  b. Write the number sentence you can use to find the estimate.

  $900 \div 30 = $ __30__

2. $3,505 \div 53$

  a. What basic fact could you use to estimate the quotient? __$35 \div 5 = 7$__

  b. Write the number sentence you can use to find the estimate.

  $3,500 \div 50 = $ __70__

3. $316 \div 82$ **4.** $1,222 \div 38$ **5.** $8,057 \div 89$
__about 4__   __about 30__   __about 90__

64 Use with pages 226–227.

180

Dividing by 2-Digit Divisors

You can use pennies to help you divide.

Divide 122 by 21.

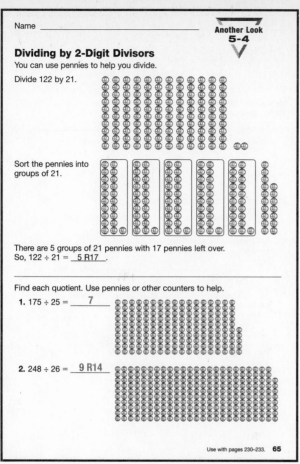

Sort the pennies into groups of 21.

There are 5 groups of 21 pennies with 17 pennies left over.

So, 122 ÷ 21 = __5 R17__ .

Find each quotient. Use pennies or other counters to help.

1. 175 ÷ 25 = __7__

2. 248 ÷ 26 = __9 R14__

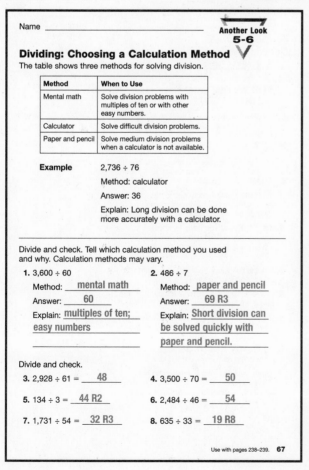

Dividing Greater Numbers

Estimation can help you divide greater numbers.

Divide 31)4,716

Where will you place the first digit of the quotient?
Since 31 < 47, the first digit goes in the hundreds place.

Look at the first 2 digits of the dividend. Guess how many times 31 will go into 47. Since 3 will only divide 4 one time, try 1.

Multiply 31 by 1 and subtract the product from 47.

$$\begin{array}{r} 31 \\ \times\ 1 \\ \hline 31 \end{array}$$

Bring down the tens digit.

$$\begin{array}{r} 1 \\ 31\overline{)4,716} \\ -31 \\ \hline 161 \end{array}$$

Now divide 31 into 161. Guess how many times 31 will go into 161. Since 16 ÷ 3 is about 5, try 5.

Multiply 31 by 5 and subtract the product from 161.

$$\begin{array}{r} 31 \\ \times\ 5 \\ \hline 155 \end{array}$$

$$\begin{array}{r} 15 \\ 31\overline{)4,716} \\ -31 \\ \hline 161 \\ -155 \\ \hline 66 \end{array}$$

Bring down the ones digit.

Guess how many times 31 will go into 66. Since 6 ÷ 3 is 2, try 2.

Multiply 31 by 2 and subtract the product from 66.

$$\begin{array}{r} 31 \\ \times\ 2 \\ \hline 62 \end{array}$$

$$\begin{array}{r} 152\ R4 \\ 31\overline{)4,716} \\ -31 \\ \hline 161 \\ -155 \\ \hline 66 \\ -62 \\ \hline 4 \end{array}$$

4,716 ÷ 31 = __152 R4__

Divide. Follow the steps above. Use a separate piece of paper if necessary.

1. 23)744 — 32 R8   **2.** 42)4,756 — 113 R10   **3.** 38)4,196 — 110 R16

Dividing: Choosing a Calculation Method

The table shows three methods for solving division.

Method	When to Use
Mental math	Solve division problems with multiples of ten or with other easy numbers.
Calculator	Solve difficult division problems.
Paper and pencil	Solve medium division problems when a calculator is not available.

Example 2,736 ÷ 76

Method: calculator

Answer: 36

Explain: Long division can be done more accurately with a calculator.

Divide and check. Tell which calculation method you used and why. Calculation methods may vary.

1. 3,600 ÷ 60

Method: __mental math__

Answer: __60__

Explain: __multiples of ten; easy numbers__

2. 486 ÷ 7

Method: __paper and pencil__

Answer: __69 R3__

Explain: __Short division can be solved quickly with paper and pencil.__

Divide and check.

3. 2,928 ÷ 61 = __48__

4. 3,500 ÷ 70 = __50__

5. 134 ÷ 3 = __44 R2__

6. 2,484 ÷ 46 = __54__

7. 1,731 ÷ 54 = __32 R3__

8. 635 ÷ 33 = __19 R8__

Zeros in the Quotient

Sometimes a quotient has a zero in it. These examples show how to handle zeros.

$$\begin{array}{r} 280\ R5 \\ 25\overline{)7,005} \\ -50 \\ \hline 200 \\ 200 \\ \hline 05 \\ -0 \\ \hline 5 \end{array}$$
5 < 25
Try 0.

$$\begin{array}{r} 302 \\ 25\overline{)7,550} \\ -75 \\ \hline 05 \\ -0 \\ \hline 50 \\ -50 \\ \hline 0 \end{array}$$
5 < 25
Try 0.

You need to place 0 in these quotients to show you have no <u>ones</u> or <u>tens</u>.

Divide and check. Use the steps as a guide.

1. 7)426 — 60 R6   **2.** 33)3,521 — 106 R23   **3.** 63)6,847 — 108 R43

4. 34)31,975 — 940 R15   **5.** 56)22,712 — 405 R32   **6.** 63)25,313 — 401 R50

7. 37)39,513 — 1,067 R34   **8.** 23)57,691 — 2,508 R7   **9.** 17)51,717 — 3,042 R3

Exploring Algebra: Using Expressions

In your book, you used algebraic expressions to represent pictures. Here you will work with algebraic expressions and variables.

Algebraic Expression $n + 7$ is an algebraic expression because it
$n + 7$ has the variable n. A variable is a letter that
↑   is used to represent a number.
variable

Evaluate $n + 7$ To *evaluate* an algebraic expression means to find
for $n = 6$ its value by replacing the variable with a number.
↓
$\boxed{6} + 7 = 13$

Evaluate each algebraic expression.

1. $8 + n$ for $n = 9$ **2.** $10 + n$ for $n = 5$
↓   ↓   ↓   ↓
$8 + \boxed{9} = \underline{17}$ $10 + \boxed{5} = \underline{15}$

3. $n - 6$ for $n = 13$ **4.** $3 \times n$ for $n = 8$
↓   ↓   ↓   ↓
$\boxed{13} - \underline{6} = \underline{7}$ $\underline{3} \times \boxed{8} = \underline{24}$

5. $n \div 2$ for $n = 18$ **6.** $n + 11$ for $n = 5$
↓   ↓   ↓   ↓
$\boxed{18} \div \underline{2} = \underline{9}$ $\boxed{5} + \underline{11} = \underline{16}$

7. $n - 12$ for $n = 15$ **8.** $n \times 5$ for $n = 4$
↓   ↓   ↓   ↓
$\boxed{15} - \underline{12} = \underline{3}$ $\boxed{4} \times \underline{5} = \underline{20}$

Analyze Strategies:
Use Objects/Act It Out

You decide to design an apartment building in the shape of a staircase. The tallest section will have 4 apartments. How many apartments will be in the building? Use cubes to represent the apartments to help solve the problem. Build a staircase.

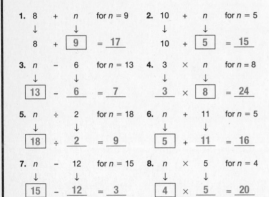

Step 1	Step 2	Step 3	Step 4
Start with 4 cubes.	Next, place 3 cubes.	Then, add 2 cubes.	Finally, place 1 cube.

Count the cubes to find out how many are used to make the staircase. __10__

Since each cube represents an the apartment, there are __10__ apartments.

Use cubes to help solve each problem.

1. Design a building in the shape of a staircase. The tallest section will have 7 apartments. How many apartments will be in the building?
__28__

2. Design a building that is in the shape of a cube. Each side of the building will be 2 apartments long.

   a. How many apartments are on the first floor? __4__

   b. How many floors high will the building be? __2__

   c. How many apartments will there be in all? __8__

Dividing Money

You can use play money or draw a money model to help you divide money. Divide $3.84 by 12.

Step 1	Step 2	Step 3
Divide the dollars into groups of 12.	Change each of the dollars to dimes. Divide the dimes into groups of 12.	Change the 2 remaining dimes to 20 pennies. Divide the pennies into groups of 12.
There are not enough dollars to divide into groups of 12.	There are 3 groups of 12 and 2 dimes remaining.	There are 2 groups of 12.

$3.84 divided by 12 is __$0.32__.

Use play money or draw a picture to divide.

1. $\overset{\$0.25}{12\overline{)\$2.75}}$ **2.** $\overset{\$1.25}{10\overline{)\$12.50}}$ **3.** $\overset{\$0.75}{12\overline{)\$9.00}}$

4. $\overset{\$0.13}{27\overline{)\$3.51}}$ **5.** $\overset{\$3.20}{15\overline{)\$48.00}}$ **6.** $\overset{\$3.19}{30\overline{)\$95.70}}$

Decision Making

★★★★ FOUR STAR CINEMA

ADMISSION
Adults $6.00
Children $3.25

MOVIE TIMES
Space and Beyond
1:00 • 3:00 • 5:00 • 7:00
Vacation of a Lifetime
1:30 • 3:30 • 5:30 •7:30
Looking for Laughter
1:15 • 3:30 • 5:45 • 8:00
City Under Siege
12:45 • 3:15 • 5:45 • 8:15

★★★★ Popcorn Specials
Large Popcorn with 10 oz. Juice → $5.50
Medium Popcorn with 6 oz. Juice → $3.50
★★★★

Use the information given to answer the questions. In all situations, assume that you must be at the theater 15 minutes before showtime.

1. If it takes 15 minutes to get to the movie theater, what time would you leave to see *Space and Beyond* at 3:00?
2:30 P.M.

2. If it is 3:00 and you have 15 minutes to travel, what movies can you see?
Vacation of a Lifetime; Looking for Laughter

3. What is the cost of admission for three adults and four children?
$31.00

4. Is $20 enough to pay for 2 adults, 2 children, and a medium popcorn special? Explain.
no; $20.00 < $22.00

5. If it takes 30 minutes to get to the theater, what is the latest time you can leave to see *City Under Siege* at 5:45?
5:00

6. If you arrive at the movie theater at 6:45, what is the earliest movie you can see?
Space and Beyond

7. Sarah wants to take 6 friends and her mother to see a movie. If all of her friends qualify for children's tickets, what will be the total cost of admission?
$28.75

Exploring Decimal Patterns in Division

In your book you used a calculator to divide decimals. Here is another way to divide decimals. When you divide a decimal by 10, 100, or 1,000, the digits in the decimal remain the same, but the decimal point moves to the left.

Examples

168.3 ÷ 10   10 has **1 zero**.   Move decimal **1 place** left.

16.83

168.3 ÷ 100   100 has **2 zeros**.   Move decimal **2 places** left.

1.683

168.3 ÷ 1,000   1,000 has **3 zeros**.   Move decimal **3 places** left.

0.1683

If there are not enough digits, add zeros to the left of the number.

3.2 ÷ 1,000   Move decimal **3 places**.   Add 2 zeros.

0.0032

Circle the letter of the correct quotient.

1. 62.5 ÷ 10   **a.** 0.625   **(b.)** 6.25   **c.** 0.0625

2. 736.4 ÷ 100   **(a.)** 7.364   **b.** 73.64   **c.** 0.7364

3. 62.15 ÷ 1,000   **a.** 6.215   **(b.)** 0.06215   **c.** 6,215

Find each quotient. Use mental math.

4. 231.8 ÷ 100 = __2.318__   **5.** 62.8 ÷ 10 = __6.28__

6. 249.2 ÷ 1,000 = __0.2492__   **7.** 44 ÷ 10 = __4.4__

8. 34.8 ÷ 100 = __0.348__   **9.** 3,841.9 ÷ 1,000 = __3.8419__

Lines and Angles

Parallel lines always lie side by side. $\overleftrightarrow{AB}$ is parallel to $\overleftrightarrow{CD}$.

Intersecting lines cross at one point. $\overleftrightarrow{EF}$ and $\overleftrightarrow{GH}$ are intersecting lines.

Perpendicular lines are intersecting lines that form square corners where they cross. $\overleftrightarrow{IJ}$ and $\overleftrightarrow{KL}$ are perpendicular.

Write the name for each pair of lines.

1. __intersecting__   **2.** __perpendicular__

3. __intersecting__   **4.** __parallel__

Exploring Measuring Angles

In your book, you classified angles using a protractor. Here is another way.

This shelf is at a right angle to the wall. The books fit the "right" way.

This shelf is at an obtuse angle, which is larger than a right angle. The books slide to the floor.

This shelf is at an acute angle, which is smaller than a right angle. The books won't fit on this shelf.

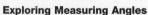

Write the name of each angle.

1. __right__   **2.** __acute__

3. __acute__   **4.** __right__

5. __obtuse__   **6.** __straight__

Triangles

You can classify triangles by the lengths of their sides and the size of their angles.

acute— all angles less than 90°   **equilateral**— sides the same length   This is an **equilateral, acute** triangle.

Not all acute triangles are equilateral.

right— one right angle   **isosceles**— two sides the same length   This is an **isosceles, right** triangle.

Not all right triangles are isosceles.

obtuse— one obtuse angle   **scalene**— no sides the same length   This is a **scalene, obtuse** triangle.

Not all obtuse triangles are scalene.

Classify each triangle by its sides and angles.

1. __isosceles;__ __acute__   **2.** __equilateral;__ __acute__   **3.** __scalene;__ __right__

4. __scalene;__ __obtuse__   **5.** __isosceles;__ __obtuse__   **6.** __equilateral;__ __acute__

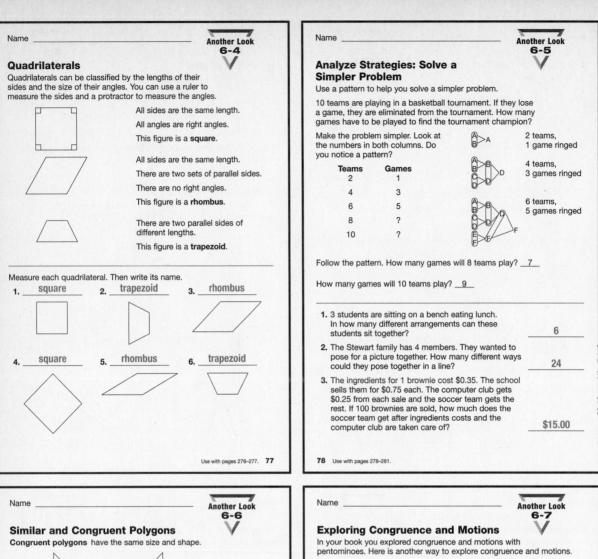

Panel 1 (top-left)

Name _____

Another Look
6-4

Quadrilaterals

Quadrilaterals can be classified by the lengths of their sides and the size of their angles. You can use a ruler to measure the sides and a protractor to measure the angles.

All sides are the same length.

All angles are right angles.

This figure is a **square**.

All sides are the same length.

There are two sets of parallel sides.

There are no right angles.

This figure is a **rhombus**.

There are two parallel sides of different lengths.

This figure is a **trapezoid**.

Measure each quadrilateral. Then write its name.

1. ___square___

2. ___trapezoid___

3. ___rhombus___

4. ___square___

5. ___rhombus___

6. ___trapezoid___

Panel 2 (top-right)

Name _____

Another Look
6-5

Analyze Strategies: Solve a Simpler Problem

Use a pattern to help you solve a simpler problem.

10 teams are playing in a basketball tournament. If they lose a game, they are eliminated from the tournament. How many games have to be played to find the tournament champion?

Make the problem simpler. Look at the numbers in both columns. Do you notice a pattern?

2 teams, 1 game ringed

4 teams, 3 games ringed

6 teams, 5 games ringed

Teams	Games
2	1
4	3
6	5
8	?
10	?

Follow the pattern. How many games will 8 teams play? ___7___

How many games will 10 teams play? ___9___

1. 3 students are sitting on a bench eating lunch. In how many different arrangements can these students sit together? ___6___

2. The Stewart family has 4 members. They wanted to pose for a picture together. How many different ways could they pose together in a line? ___24___

3. The ingredients for 1 brownie cost $0.35. The school sells them for $0.75 each. The computer club gets $0.25 from each sale and the soccer team gets the rest. If 100 brownies are sold, how much does the soccer team get after ingredients costs and the computer club are taken care of? ___$15.00___

Panel 3 (bottom-left)

Name _____

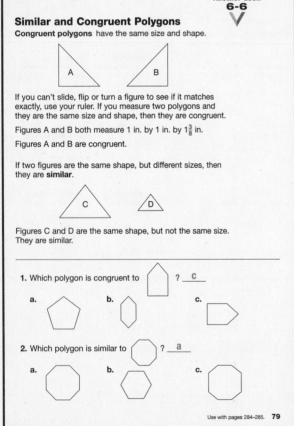
Another Look
6-6

Similar and Congruent Polygons

Congruent polygons have the same size and shape.

If you can't slide, flip or turn a figure to see if it matches exactly, use your ruler. If you measure two polygons and they are the same size and shape, then they are congruent.

Figures A and B both measure 1 in. by 1 in. by $1\frac{3}{8}$ in.

Figures A and B are congruent.

If two figures are the same shape, but different sizes, then they are **similar**.

Figures C and D are the same shape, but not the same size. They are similar.

1. Which polygon is congruent to ⬠ ? ___c___

   a.   b.   c.

2. Which polygon is similar to ⬡ ? ___a___

   a.   b.   c.

Panel 4 (bottom-right)

Name _____

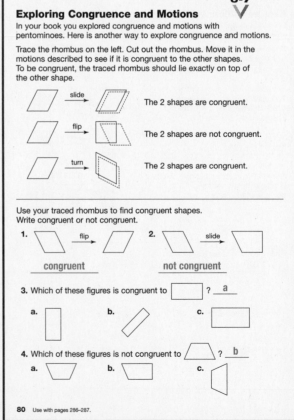
Another Look
6-7

Exploring Congruence and Motions

In your book you explored congruence and motions with pentominoes. Here is another way to explore congruence and motions.

Trace the rhombus on the left. Cut out the rhombus. Move it in the motions described to see if it is congruent to the other shapes. To be congruent, the traced rhombus should lie exactly on top of the other shape.

slide → The 2 shapes are congruent.

flip → The 2 shapes are not congruent.

turn → The 2 shapes are congruent.

Use your traced rhombus to find congruent shapes. Write congruent or not congruent.

1. flip → ___congruent___

2. slide → ___not congruent___

3. Which of these figures is congruent to ▭ ? ___a___

   a.   b.   c.

4. Which of these figures is not congruent to ▱ ? ___b___

   a.   b.   c.

Exploring Line Symmetry

In your book you explored line symmetry by using grid paper. Here is another way to explore line symmetry.

A line of symmetry is a fold line when a figure is folded in half.

This figure has 1 line of symmetry. There is only one way to fold it exactly in half.

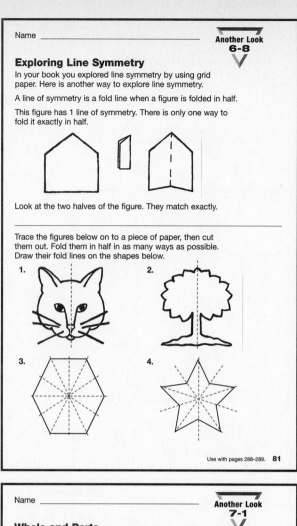

Look at the two halves of the figure. They match exactly.

Trace the figures below on to a piece of paper, then cut them out. Fold them in half in as many ways as possible. Draw their fold lines on the shapes below.

1.
2.

3.
4.

Decision Making

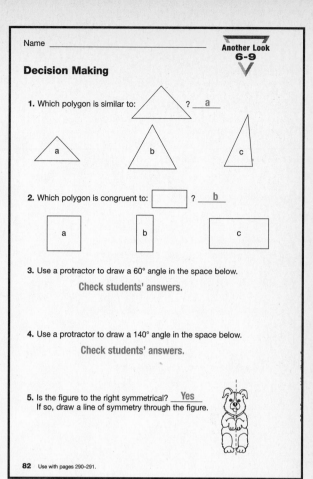

1. Which polygon is similar to: △ ? ___a___

2. Which polygon is congruent to: ▭ ? ___b___

3. Use a protractor to draw a 60° angle in the space below.

Check students' answers.

4. Use a protractor to draw a 140° angle in the space below.

Check students' answers.

5. Is the figure to the right symmetrical? ___Yes___
If so, draw a line of symmetry through the figure.

Whole and Parts

Writing fractions to describe a part or parts of something is easy when you follow these steps.

Step 1 Count the number of parts there are in all.

There are ___4___ parts in the box. This number is the **denominator**, the bottom number of a fraction. $\frac{?}{4}$

Step 2 Count the number of parts shaded.

There are ___2___ shaded parts in the box. This number is the **numerator**, the top number of a fraction. $\frac{2}{?}$

Step 3 The fraction that describes the shaded parts of the entire box is: $\frac{2}{4}$

Follow the steps to write fractions:
a. to describe each shaded part.
b. to describe each unshaded part.

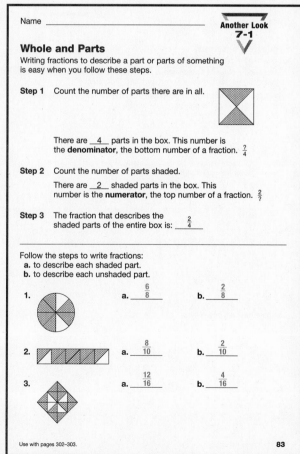

1.   a. $\frac{6}{8}$ b. $\frac{2}{8}$

2.   a. $\frac{8}{10}$ b. $\frac{2}{10}$

3.   a. $\frac{12}{16}$ b. $\frac{4}{16}$

Exploring Equivalent Fractions

In your book, you explored equivalent fractions using fraction strips. Here is another way to work with equivalent fractions.

You can draw pictures to help you see if fractions are equivalent.

$\frac{3}{4}$ $\frac{2}{3}$ $\frac{6}{8}$

Step 1 Draw the same shape for each fraction. Choose a shape, like a rectangle, that is easy to divide into parts.

Step 2 Divide each shape into equal parts. Remember the denominator describes the total number of parts.

Step 3 Shade in the number of parts found in the numerator.

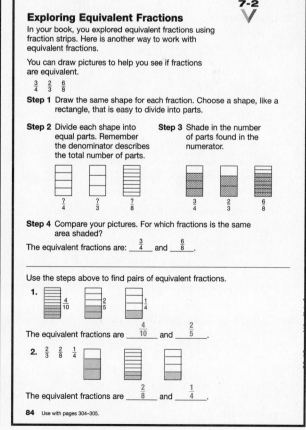

$\frac{?}{4}$ $\frac{?}{3}$ $\frac{?}{8}$ $\frac{3}{4}$ $\frac{2}{3}$ $\frac{6}{8}$

Step 4 Compare your pictures. For which fractions is the same area shaded?

The equivalent fractions are: $\frac{3}{4}$ and $\frac{6}{8}$.

Use the steps above to find pairs of equivalent fractions.

1. $\frac{4}{10}$ $\frac{2}{5}$ $\frac{1}{4}$

The equivalent fractions are $\frac{4}{10}$ and $\frac{2}{5}$.

2. $\frac{2}{3}$ $\frac{2}{8}$ $\frac{1}{4}$

The equivalent fractions are $\frac{2}{8}$ and $\frac{1}{4}$.

Patterns with Equivalent Fractions

You can use pictures to help you identify equivalent fractions.

Find an equivalent fraction with a denominator of 12.

$\frac{2}{3}$

Draw a picture to represent the fraction.

Divide the shape into 12 equal parts.

$\frac{}{12}$

Count the number of shaded squares. This is the numerator of the equivalent fraction.

$\frac{2}{3} = \frac{\boxed{8}}{12}$

Use the steps above to find equivalent fractions.

1. Find an equivalent fraction with a denominator of 10.

$\frac{3}{5} = \frac{\boxed{6}}{10}$

2. Find an equivalent fraction with a denominator of 9.

$\frac{1}{3} = \frac{\boxed{3}}{9}$

Find equivalent fractions with a denominator of 6.

3. $\frac{2}{3} = \frac{\boxed{4}}{6}$ **4.** $\frac{1}{2} = \frac{\boxed{3}}{6}$ **5.** $\frac{1}{3} = \frac{\boxed{2}}{6}$

Find equivalent fractions with a denominator of 12.

6. $\frac{1}{6} = \frac{\boxed{2}}{12}$ **7.** $\frac{1}{2} = \frac{\boxed{6}}{12}$ **8.** $\frac{3}{4} = \frac{\boxed{9}}{12}$

Greatest Common Factor

You can use a table to find the greatest common factor of two numbers.

Find the greatest common factor of 12 and 16. Complete the tables for all possible factors of each number.

Circle all factors that appear in both charts. The greatest factor circled is the greatest common factor.

The greatest common factor of 12 and 16 is ___4___.

Use the steps above to find the greatest common factors of each pair of numbers.

1. The greatest common factor of 18 and 24 is ___6___.

2. The greatest common factor of 21 and 28 is ___7___.

Factors of 18	Factors of 24
① 18	① 24
② 9	② 12
③ 6	③ 8
	4 ⑥

Factors of 21	Factors of 28
① 21	① 28
3 ⑦	2 14
	4 ⑦

3. The greatest common factor of 25 and 30 is ___5___.

4. The greatest common factor of 16 and 20 is ___4___.

Factors of 25	Factors of 30
① 25	① 30
5 ⑤	2 15
	3 10
	⑤ 6

Factors of 16	Factors of 20
① 16	① 20
② 8	② 10
④ 4	④ 5

Simplest Form

Is $\frac{6}{12}$ in its simplest form?

Step 1 Ask: Is 1 the greatest common factor of the numerator and denominator?

$3 \times 2 = 6$ $6 \times 2 = 12$

2 is a common factor.

Step 2 Divide the numerator and denominator by the common factor, 2.

$\frac{6}{12} = \frac{\cancel{6}^{3} \times 3}{\cancel{12}^{6} \times 6} = \frac{3}{6}$

Step 3 Continue to look for common factors. Divide the numerator and denominator by the common factor. Continue until the only common factor is 1.

3 is a common factor.

$\frac{3}{6} = \frac{\cancel{3}^{1} \times 1}{\cancel{6}^{2} \times 2} = \frac{1}{2}$

The only factor in common to 1 and 2 is 1, so $\frac{1}{2}$ is in simplest form.

---

1. Circle fractions with 2 as a common factor. Underline fractions with 3 as a common factor.

$\frac{2}{4}$ $\frac{6}{8}$ $\frac{3}{9}$ $\frac{4}{12}$ $\frac{2}{10}$

2. Circle fractions that are in simplest form.

$\frac{1}{8}$ $\frac{2}{6}$ $\frac{6}{9}$ $\frac{2}{3}$ $\frac{4}{5}$

Write each fraction in simplest form.

3. $\frac{12}{18}$ ___$\frac{2}{3}$___   **4.** $\frac{9}{12}$ ___$\frac{3}{4}$___   **5.** $\frac{16}{20}$ ___$\frac{4}{5}$___

6. $\frac{14}{18}$ ___$\frac{7}{9}$___   **7.** $\frac{6}{10}$ ___$\frac{3}{5}$___   **8.** $\frac{4}{16}$ ___$\frac{1}{4}$___

Exploring Comparing and Ordering Fractions

In your book, you used fraction strips to compare and order fractions. Here are some rules to help you compare and order fractions.

Rule 1 If 2 fractions have a numerator of 1, the fraction with the lesser denominator is greater.

$\boxed{\frac{1}{2}}$ $\boxed{\frac{1}{3}}$ $2 < 3$

$\frac{1}{2} > \frac{1}{3}$

Rule 2 If 2 fractions have the same numerator, the fraction with the lesser denominator is greater.

$\boxed{\frac{2}{7}}$ $\boxed{\frac{2}{8}}$ $7 < 8$

$\frac{2}{7} > \frac{2}{8}$

Rule 3 If 2 fractions have the same denominator, the fraction with the greater numerator is greater.

$\boxed{\frac{3}{5}}$ $\boxed{\frac{2}{5}}$ $3 > 2$

$\frac{3}{5} > \frac{2}{5}$

Compare the fractions. Which fraction is greater?

1. $\frac{1}{4}$ $\frac{1}{8}$ **2.** $\frac{3}{5}$ $\frac{3}{4}$ **3.** $\frac{4}{9}$ $\frac{8}{9}$

     $\frac{1}{4}$ $\frac{3}{4}$ $\frac{8}{9}$

Compare the fractions. Write > or <. Use the three rules to help you.

4. $\frac{3}{10}$ $\boxed{>}$ $\frac{3}{11}$ **5.** $\frac{2}{5}$ $\boxed{<}$ $\frac{3}{5}$ **6.** $\frac{5}{6}$ $\boxed{>}$ $\frac{5}{10}$

7. $\frac{4}{9}$ $\boxed{<}$ $\frac{4}{6}$ **8.** $\frac{7}{8}$ $\boxed{>}$ $\frac{5}{8}$ **9.** $\frac{1}{2}$ $\boxed{>}$ $\frac{1}{4}$

Comparing and Ordering Fractions

Compare $\frac{2}{3}$ and $\frac{3}{4}$.

How do you compare fractions like $\frac{2}{3}$ and $\frac{3}{4}$ that have different denominators and numerators?

Step 1 Find a common denominator by multiplying the denominators. A common denominator for $\frac{2}{3}$ and $\frac{3}{4}$ is 3×4 or 12.

Step 2 Change to equivalent fractions.

$\frac{2 \times 4}{3 \times 4} = \frac{8}{12}$

$\frac{2}{3}$ and $\frac{8}{12}$ are equivalent.

$\frac{3 \times 3}{4 \times 3} = \frac{9}{12}$

$\frac{3}{4}$ and $\frac{9}{12}$ are equivalent.

Step 3 You can see from the pictures that $\frac{9}{12} > \frac{8}{12}$. So, $\frac{3}{4} > \frac{2}{3}$.

Change to equivalent fractions. Then circle the greater fraction.

1. $\frac{1}{2} = \frac{5}{10}$ $\frac{3}{5} = \boxed{\frac{6}{10}}$ 2. $\frac{5}{9} = \boxed{\frac{10}{18}}$ $\frac{1}{3} = \frac{6}{18}$

Compare. Write >, <, or = to complete. Use equivalent fractions.

3. $\frac{1}{4} \;\boxed{<}\; \frac{3}{8}$ 4. $\frac{2}{3} \;\boxed{=}\; \frac{6}{9}$ 5. $\frac{7}{8} \;\boxed{>}\; \frac{7}{9}$

6. $\frac{1}{6} \;\boxed{>}\; \frac{1}{8}$ 7. $\frac{5}{9} \;\boxed{>}\; \frac{1}{3}$ 8. $\frac{8}{9} \;\boxed{>}\; \frac{2}{3}$

Analyze Strategies: Make a Table

To solve some problems, it helps to put the data in a table. Read the problem below.

Mr. Garcia, found a great sale on his favorite shirt. The sale was two shirts for $15.00. He had $50 with him to purchase the shirts. How many shirts could he purchase?

numbers of shirts	2	4	6	8
shirt price	$15	$30	$45	$60

Look for a pattern. If 2 shirts cost $15, 4 shirts will cost twice as much. So, 4 shirts will cost $2 \times \$15 = \$30$.

Complete the table. How many shirts can Mr. Garcia buy for $50? __6__

Solve by making a table.

1. The Smith family had 3 left-handed family members for every 4 right-handed family members. As the family grows, how many left-handed family members will there be when there are 32 right-handed family members, if the pattern continues?

left-handed family members	3	6	9	12	15	18	21	24
right-handed family members	4	8	12	16	20	24	28	32

2. For every scoop of ice cream Sam sells, he sells 3 ice cream floats. How many floats did he sell when he sold 8 scoops of ice cream?

scoops	1	2	3	4	5	6	7	8
floats	3	6	9	12	15	18	21	24

Exploring Mixed Numbers

In your book you used fraction strips to explore mixed numbers. Here is another way to see mixed numbers.

Make a drawing to show $3\frac{5}{8}$.

Draw 3 whole shapes to represent the whole number 3.

Draw one more whole shape. Divide it into the number of equal parts shown in the denominator. Shade the number of parts shown in the numerator.

Match the pictures with the correct **mixed numbers** from the box.

4	$2\frac{1}{4}$	$1\frac{1}{3}$	$3\frac{4}{6}$	$2\frac{2}{6}$	$1\frac{2}{5}$

1. $2\frac{2}{6}$
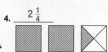

2. $1\frac{1}{3}$

3. $3\frac{4}{6}$

4. $2\frac{1}{4}$
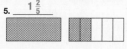

Write the mixed or whole number that names the shaded part.

5. $1\frac{2}{5}$

6. 4

Mixed Numbers

You can use drawings to help you write mixed numbers and improper fractions.

Write $2\frac{1}{8}$ as an improper fraction.

Draw $2\frac{1}{8}$. Divide each whole into eighths.

Count the eighths. $2\frac{1}{8} = \frac{17}{8}$

Draw a picture for each mixed number. Then write the mixed number as an improper fraction.

1. $2\frac{1}{2} = \boxed{\frac{5}{2}}$

2. $4\frac{3}{4} = \boxed{\frac{19}{4}}$

3. $3\frac{2}{3} = \boxed{\frac{11}{3}}$

4. $3\frac{3}{8} = \boxed{\frac{27}{8}}$

Exploring Comparing and Ordering Mixed Numbers

In your book you used fraction strips to compare and order mixed numbers. Here is another way to compare and order mixed numbers.

Example 1

Use a number line to compare $2\frac{5}{8}$ and $2\frac{3}{4}$. On a number line, $2\frac{5}{8}$ and $2\frac{3}{4}$ are between 2 and 3.

What is the common denominator of $\frac{5}{8}$ and $\frac{3}{4}$? __8__

Divide the space on the number line into 8 parts.

Mark $2\frac{5}{8}$ and $2\frac{3}{4}$ on the number line.

Because $2\frac{3}{4}$ is closer to 3, $2\frac{3}{4}$ is greater than $2\frac{5}{8}$. $2\frac{3}{4} > 2\frac{5}{8}$

Example 2

Use a number line to put $1\frac{3}{4}$, $1\frac{2}{3}$, and $1\frac{5}{6}$ in order from least to greatest.

All three numbers are between which two whole numbers? __1 and 2__

What is the common denominator? __12__

Show the three numbers on the number line.

List the three numbers in order from least to greatest. $1\frac{2}{3}$; $1\frac{3}{4}$; $1\frac{5}{6}$

Compare. Use > or <.

1. $2\frac{1}{2}$ and $1\frac{3}{4}$ $2\frac{1}{2} > 1\frac{3}{4}$
2. $3\frac{1}{3}$ and $3\frac{1}{2}$ $3\frac{1}{3} < 3\frac{1}{2}$
3. $1\frac{3}{4}$ and $1\frac{7}{8}$ $1\frac{3}{4} < 1\frac{7}{8}$
4. $\frac{3}{2}$ and $\frac{11}{6}$ $\frac{3}{2} < \frac{11}{6}$

Write in order from least to greatest.

5. $2\frac{3}{4}$, $2\frac{1}{6}$, $2\frac{1}{2}$ $2\frac{1}{6}$, $2\frac{1}{2}$, $2\frac{3}{4}$
6. $\frac{13}{3}$, $\frac{9}{2}$, $\frac{12}{5}$ $\frac{12}{5}$, $\frac{13}{3}$, $\frac{9}{2}$

Understanding Percent

The word "per cent" means "out of one hundred."
For example $\frac{30}{100}$ is 30 out of 100, or 30%.

How many squares are there in the drawing? __100__

How many squares are shaded? __30__

The shaded part can be described as:

30 out of 100 $\frac{30}{100}$ 30%

1. a. How many squares are in the drawing? __100__

   b. How many squares are shaded? __15__

   c. The shaded part can be described as __15__ out of __100__.

   d. Describe the shaded part with a fraction. $\frac{15}{100}$

   e. Describe the shaded part with a percent. __15%__

Write the percent shaded in each drawing.

2. __25%__   3. __44%__

Rewrite the fractions as a percent.

4. $\frac{35}{100}$ __35%__
5. $\frac{42}{100}$ __42%__
6. $\frac{63}{100}$ __63%__
7. $\frac{58}{100}$ __58%__
8. $\frac{77}{100}$ __77%__
9. $\frac{21}{100}$ __21%__

Connecting Fractions, Decimals, and Percents

There are 100 rides on the bus pass, and 25 of them have been used.

Write a fraction, a decimal, and a percent to tell how many rides have been used.

Fraction: $\frac{25}{100}$

Decimal: __0.25__   Use a decimal point to show hundredths.

Percent: __25%__   Use a percent sign to mean "out of 100."

Write a fraction, a decimal and a percent to tell how many rides are left on the bus pass.

Fraction: $\frac{75}{100}$

Decimal: __0.75__   Use a decimal point to show hundredths.

Percent: __75%__   Use a percent sign to mean "out of 100."

Write a fraction, a decimal, and a percent that name each shaded part and unshaded part.

1. shaded part $\frac{40}{100}$, 0.40, 40%
   unshaded part $\frac{60}{100}$, 0.60, 60%

2. shaded part $\frac{15}{100}$, 0.15, 15%
   unshaded part $\frac{85}{100}$, 0.85, 85%

3. shaded part $\frac{50}{100}$, 0.50, 50%
   unshaded part $\frac{50}{100}$, 0.50, 50%

4. shaded part $\frac{4}{100}$, 0.04, 4%
   unshaded part $\frac{96}{100}$, 0.96, 96%

Decision Making

The table shows the results of a survey Mr. Andrews took of the students in his class.

Which Kind of Story Do You Like Best?	
Stories about animals	╫╫ ╫╫
Stories about people	╫╫ ╫╫ ╫╫

Count the total number of tally marks. How many students were surveyed? __25__

Ten of the students liked stories about animals best, so $\frac{10}{25}$ of the students chose stories about animals.

To write $\frac{10}{25}$ as a percent, multiply numerator and denominator by 4, because $25 \times 4 = 100$; $\frac{10}{25} = \frac{40}{100}$. Of the 25 students, 40% chose stories about animals.

You can find the number of students who chose stories about people by subtracting 40% from 100%. Of the 25 students, 60% chose stories about people.

1. Make a survey of 10 students in your class. Ask them which kind of stories they like best, stories about animals or stories about people.

   a. How can you write the results of your survey as percents?

   Multiply numerator and denominator by 10.

   b. How do your results compare with the results in Mr. Andrews' class?

   Possible answer: My results are similar.

2. Compare your results in Exercise 1 with the results of other students in your class. Are your results similar or are they different?

   Possible answer: My results are different.

Panel 1 (top-left)

Adding and Subtracting Fractions with Like Denominators

Drawing pictures can help you add and subtract fractions with like denominators.

$\frac{7}{8} + \frac{5}{8}$

Step 1 Look at the denominator. Draw a shape divided into the number of parts in the denominator.

Step 2 Shade in the number of parts described by the first fraction.

Step 3 a. To add, shade in the second fraction. Draw another shape if you run out of sections to shade. Then count the number of shaded pieces in all. Remember to count a fully shaded piece as one whole.

$\frac{7}{8} + \frac{5}{8} = 1\frac{4}{8} = 1\frac{1}{2}$

$\frac{5}{8} - \frac{2}{8}$

b. To subtract, shade the second fraction over the first fraction. Then count the number of pieces shaded once.

$\frac{5}{8} - \frac{2}{8} = \frac{3}{8}$

Divide each rectangle into equal parts and use shading to help you find each sum or difference. Simplify.

1. $\frac{3}{9} + \frac{3}{9} = \frac{2}{3}$

2. $\frac{7}{9} - \frac{4}{9} = \frac{1}{3}$

3. $\frac{7}{10} + \frac{3}{10} = 1$

4. $\frac{8}{10} - \frac{2}{10} = \frac{3}{5}$

Panel 2 (top-right)

Exploring Adding Fractions

In your book, you explored sums using fraction strips. Here is another way to add fractions with unlike denominators.

$\frac{3}{4} + \frac{3}{8}$

You can use a ruler to help you find the sum.

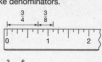

$\frac{3}{4} = \frac{6}{8}$

$\frac{6}{8} + \frac{3}{8} = \frac{9}{8} = 1\frac{1}{8}$

Use the ruler provided to help you find each sum.

1. $\frac{1}{4} + \frac{1}{2} = \frac{3}{4}$

2. $\frac{5}{8} + \frac{1}{4} = \frac{7}{8}$

3. $\frac{3}{4} + \frac{1}{8} = \frac{7}{8}$

4. $\frac{1}{4} + \frac{1}{8} = \frac{3}{8}$

5. $\frac{7}{8} + \frac{3}{4} = 1\frac{5}{8}$

6. $\frac{1}{2} + \frac{5}{8} = 1\frac{1}{8}$

Panel 3 (bottom-left)

Least Common Denominator

Find the least common denominator (LCD) for $\frac{1}{3}$ and $\frac{3}{4}$.

The denominator of $\frac{1}{3}$ is 3. The denominator of $\frac{3}{4}$ is 4.

What is the least number that is a multiple of both 3 and 4? This number is the least common denominator.

Find some multiples of 3:	Find some multiples of 4:
$3 \times 1 = 3$	$4 \times 1 = 4$
$3 \times 2 = 6$	$4 \times 2 = 8$
$3 \times 3 = 9$	$4 \times 3 = 12$
$3 \times 4 = 12$	$4 \times 4 = 16$
$3 \times 5 = 15$	$4 \times 5 = 20$
$3 \times 6 = 18$	$4 \times 6 = 24$
$3 \times 7 = 21$
$3 \times 8 = 24$

Some multiples of 3 are: 3, 6, 9, 12, 15, 18, 21, 24.

Some multiples of 4 are: 4, 8, 12, 16, 20, 24.

Which numbers above are multiples of both 3 and 4? __12 and 24__

Which of the two multiples is the lesser number? __12__

So, the least common denominator of $\frac{1}{3}$ and $\frac{3}{4}$

Find the least common denominator (LCD) for each pair of fractions.

1. $\frac{3}{5}$ and $\frac{1}{4}$

a. List some multiples of 5. Start with the least numbers.

5, 10, 15, 20, 25, 30, 35, 40

b. List some multiples of 4. Start with the least numbers.

4, 8, 12, 16, 20, 24, 28, 32, 36, 40

c. Which numbers above are multiples of both 5 and 4? 20, 40

d. What is the LCD for $\frac{3}{5}$ and $\frac{1}{4}$? 20

2. $\frac{5}{6}$ and $\frac{3}{7}$ __42__   **3.** $\frac{1}{5}$ and $\frac{2}{3}$ __15__   **4.** $\frac{1}{8}$ and $\frac{1}{6}$ __24__

Panel 4 (bottom-right)

Adding Fractions

Find $\frac{3}{4} + \frac{1}{6}$.

One number that you can always use as a common denominator is the product of the denominators.

Find the equivalent fractions by multiplying each fraction by the other fraction's denominator.

$\frac{3 \times 6}{4 \times 6} = \frac{18}{24}$

$\frac{1 \times 4}{6 \times 4} = \frac{4}{24}$

Add the equivalent fractions.

$\frac{18}{24}$

$+ \frac{4}{24}$

$\frac{22}{24}$

Simplify by dividing by a common factor.

$\frac{22 \div 2}{24 \div 2} = \frac{11}{12}$

Follow the same steps to find each sum.

1. Add $\frac{2}{3}$ and $\frac{1}{4}$.

a. Write the equivalent fractions.

$\frac{2 \times 4}{3 \times 4} = \frac{8}{12}$

$\frac{1 \times 3}{4 \times 3} = \frac{3}{12}$

b. Add the equivalent fractions.

$\frac{8}{12}$

$+ \frac{3}{12}$

$\frac{11}{12}$

2. $\frac{1}{5}$ $+ \frac{5}{6}$ $\frac{31}{30} = 1\frac{1}{30}$

3. $\frac{3}{4}$ $+ \frac{5}{8}$ $\frac{44}{32} = 1\frac{3}{8}$

4. $\frac{1}{8}$ $+ \frac{1}{3}$ $\frac{11}{24}$

5. $\frac{8}{9}$ $+ \frac{1}{6}$ $\frac{57}{54} = 1\frac{1}{18}$

Panel 1

Name _____

Another Look
8-5

Exploring Subtracting Fractions

In your book, you explored differences using fraction strips.
Here is another way to subtract fractions with unlike denominators.

$\frac{3}{8} - \frac{1}{4}$

You can find the LCD (8) and draw pictures to help you find the difference.

Find equivalent fractions by using the LCD. Draw
a shape divided into the same number of equal parts
as the LCD.

Shade in the number of parts found $\frac{3}{8} = \frac{3}{8}$ $\frac{1}{4} = \frac{2}{8}$
in the greater numerator. (3) Cross off
the number of parts found in the
lesser numerator. (2)

Count the number of pieces shaded but not crossed out (1).

$\frac{3}{8} - \frac{1}{4} = \frac{1}{8}$

Use the shapes provided to help you find each difference.

1. $\frac{1}{2} - \frac{1}{4} = \frac{1}{4}$ **2.** $\frac{5}{6} - \frac{2}{3} = \frac{1}{6}$

3. $\frac{7}{8} - \frac{3}{4} = \frac{1}{8}$ **4.** $\frac{2}{3} - \frac{1}{2} = \frac{1}{6}$

Use with pages 358–359.   **101**

Panel 2

Name _____

Another Look
8-6

Subtracting Fractions

You can use drawings to help you subtract fractions.

Find the difference of $\frac{4}{5}$ and $\frac{1}{2}$. $\frac{4}{5} - \frac{1}{2}$

Step 1   Find the LCM, or least common multiple, of 5 and 2.

2	4	6	8	⑩	12
5	⑩	15	20	25	30

The LCM of 5 and 2 is 10.

Draw 2 rectangles and divide them into 10 equal parts.

Step 2   Divide the first rectangle into 5ths.

Divide the second rectangle in half.

Step 3   Shade $\frac{4}{5}$ of the first rectangle and $\frac{1}{2}$ of the second. Notice that the shaded parts are the same size Write the equivalent fractions.

$\frac{4}{5} = \frac{8}{10}$ $\frac{1}{2} = \frac{5}{10}$

Step 4

Subtract the numerators and simplify if possible.

$\frac{8}{10} - \frac{5}{10} = \frac{3}{10}$

Find the difference. Simplify. Use drawings to help you.

1. $\frac{3}{4} = \frac{9}{12}$
$\frac{1}{3} = \frac{4}{12}$
$\frac{5}{12}$

2. $\frac{2}{3} = \frac{4}{6}$
$\frac{1}{2} = \frac{3}{6}$
$\frac{1}{6}$

3. $\frac{3}{5} - \frac{5}{10} = \frac{1}{10}$ **4.** $\frac{1}{2} - \frac{3}{8} = \frac{1}{8}$

102   Use with pages 360–361.

Panel 3

Name _____

Another Look
8-7

Analyze Word Problems: Too Much or Too Little Information

The swim team practices for $\frac{1}{3}$ hr between 2 P.M. and 3 P.M. The track team runs for less than an hour between 2 and 3 P.M. How much longer do the swimmers practice than the runners?

Ask yourself:

What do I know?

The swim team practices ___$\frac{1}{3}$___ hour.

The track team runs ___don't know___ hours.

What do I need to find out?

___How much longer the swim team practices than the track team___

Can I find the information I need?

___No, the part of the hour the track team runs is not given.___

Write if each problem has too much or too little information. Solve if possible. Tell what is needed if you can't solve.

1. One box weighed $\frac{7}{8}$ lb. The box next to it weighed more than 1 lb. Find the difference in their weights.

___too little information; need to know weight of the second box___

2. The cook at the diner scrambled $\frac{1}{2}$ of the eggs served. One-fourth of the eggs were fried, and $\frac{1}{8}$ were boiled. How many eggs are left?

___too little information; need to know the number of eggs the cook started with___

3. The park has 10 swings, of which $\frac{2}{5}$ are broken. Half the swings have metal seats and $\frac{1}{10}$ of the swings have wooden seats. How many more swings have metal seats than wooden seats?

___too much information; $\frac{2}{5}$ which is 4 swings___

Use with pages 364–365.   **103**

Panel 4

Name _____

Another Look
8-8

Exploring Adding and Subtracting Mixed Numbers

In your book you added and subtracted mixed numbers using fraction strips. Here is another way to find sums and differences of mixed numbers.

Example 1 $2\frac{3}{4} - 1\frac{1}{4}$

Draw a picture to show $2\frac{3}{4}$.

Draw an X through one of the small squares to subtract $\frac{1}{4}$.

Draw an X through one of the large squares to subtract 1.

Example 2 $2\frac{1}{2} - \frac{1}{4}$

Draw a picture to show $2\frac{1}{2}$.

So you can subtract $\frac{1}{4}$, divide the square on the right into fourths.

Draw an X through one of the small squares to subtract $\frac{1}{4}$.

Write the fraction that describes the shaded portion remaining.

$2\frac{3}{4} - 1\frac{1}{4} = 1\frac{1}{2}$ $2\frac{1}{2} - \frac{1}{4} = 2\frac{1}{4}$

Add or subtract the mixed numbers. Draw pictures to help. Simplify.

1. $\begin{array}{r} 1\frac{1}{4} \\ + 3\frac{1}{4} \\ \hline 4\frac{1}{2} \end{array}$

2. $\begin{array}{r} 3\frac{3}{4} \\ - 2\frac{1}{4} \\ \hline 1\frac{1}{2} \end{array}$ **3.** $\begin{array}{r} 2\frac{1}{2} \\ + 1\frac{1}{2} \\ \hline 4 \end{array}$ **4.** $\begin{array}{r} 2\frac{1}{4} \\ + 4\frac{1}{2} \\ \hline 6\frac{3}{4} \end{array}$ **5.** $\begin{array}{r} 1\frac{1}{2} \\ - \frac{1}{4} \\ \hline 1\frac{1}{4} \end{array}$

104   Use with pages 368–369.

190

Name _____

Estimating Sums and Differences
Round to estimate the sum.

$1\frac{3}{4} + 2\frac{1}{4}$

$\frac{3}{4}$ is greater than $\frac{1}{2}$, so $\frac{3}{4}$ rounds to 1.

$\frac{1}{4}$ is less than $\frac{1}{2}$, so $\frac{1}{4}$ rounds to 0.

$1\frac{3}{4} + 2\frac{1}{4}$

$1\frac{3}{4}$ is about 2.

$2\frac{1}{4}$ is about 2.

Add the two numbers to estimate the answer. $2 + 2 = 4$

Estimate each sum or difference. Round each mixed number.

1. $7\frac{1}{2} + 6\frac{1}{4}$ $\frac{1}{2}$ rounds to __1__

                $\frac{1}{4}$ rounds to __0__

So, $7\frac{1}{2} + 6\frac{1}{4}$ is about __8__ + __6__ = __14__

2. $5\frac{2}{3} - 2\frac{1}{3}$ $\frac{2}{3}$ rounds to __1__

                $\frac{1}{3}$ rounds to __0__

So, $5\frac{2}{3} - 2\frac{1}{3}$ is about __6__ - __2__ = __4__

Possible estimates given.

3. $8\frac{1}{4} + 2\frac{3}{4} =$ __11__   **4.** $5\frac{1}{2} + 2\frac{2}{5} =$ __8__

5. $9\frac{5}{8} - 1\frac{3}{4} =$ __8__   **6.** $8\frac{1}{4} - 6\frac{1}{3} =$ __2__

7. $8\frac{5}{6} - 4\frac{2}{3} =$ __4__   **8.** $7\frac{1}{5} + 1\frac{2}{3} =$ __9__

9. $6\frac{3}{8} - 4\frac{7}{8} =$ __1__   **10.** $3\frac{4}{5} + 9\frac{1}{3} =$ __13__

11. $9\frac{1}{6} - 1\frac{2}{5} =$ __8__   **12.** $6\frac{1}{3} - 5\frac{7}{8} =$ __0__

Name _____

Adding and Subtracting Mixed Numbers
You can use drawings to help you add and subtract mixed numbers.

$3\frac{3}{4}$
$+ 5\frac{1}{3}$

Find the LCM of 4 and 3.

The LCM is 12.

Divide each of the fraction drawings into 12 pieces.

Use your drawings to write equivalent fractions.

$\frac{3}{4} = \frac{9}{12}$

$\frac{1}{3} = \frac{4}{12}$

Then add.

$3\frac{3}{4} = 3\frac{9}{12}$
$+ 5\frac{1}{3} = + 5\frac{4}{12}$
$\overline{8\frac{13}{12}} = 8 + 1\frac{1}{12} = 9\frac{1}{12}$

$3\frac{3}{4} + 5\frac{1}{3} = 9\frac{1}{12}$

Find the sums or differences. Draw pictures to help.

1.
$6\frac{3}{5} = 6\frac{6}{10}$
$- 4\frac{3}{10} = - 4\frac{3}{10}$
$\overline{2\frac{3}{10}}$

2.
$3\frac{2}{3} = 3\frac{8}{12}$
$+ 4\frac{3}{4} = + 4\frac{9}{12}$
$\overline{7\frac{17}{12}} = 8\frac{5}{12}$

3.
$5\frac{4}{5}$
$- 1\frac{1}{2}$
$\overline{4\frac{3}{10}}$

4.
$4\frac{1}{2}$
$+ 2\frac{3}{4}$
$\overline{7\frac{1}{4}}$

5.
$2\frac{1}{2}$
$- 1\frac{2}{5}$
$\overline{1\frac{1}{10}}$

Name _____

Adding Mixed Numbers
Find $2\frac{1}{4} + 1\frac{1}{2} + 4\frac{5}{6}$.

       $2\frac{1}{4}$

First you must change the fractions so they all have the same denominator.

       $1\frac{1}{2}$

     $+ 4\frac{5}{6}$

Find the number that is divisible by all three denominators. This number is the least common denominator (LCD).

The denominators are 4, 2, and 6. What is the least number divisible by 4, 2, and 6? 12 is divisible by 4, 2, and 6. **12** is the **least common denominator**.

Write each fraction as an equivalent fraction with the least common denominator.

$\frac{1}{4} = \frac{?}{12}$ $12 \div 4 = 3, 3 \times 1 = 3$, so $\frac{1}{4} = \frac{3}{12}$

$\frac{1}{2} = \frac{?}{12}$ $12 \div 2 = 6, 6 \times 1 = 6$, so $\frac{1}{2} = \frac{6}{12}$

$\frac{5}{6} = \frac{?}{12}$ $12 \div 6 = 2, 2 \times 5 = 10$, so $\frac{5}{6} = \frac{10}{12}$

       $2\frac{3}{12}$

       $1\frac{6}{12}$

    $+ 4\frac{10}{12}$ Simplify

     $\overline{7\frac{19}{12}}$ $\frac{19}{12} = 1\frac{7}{12}$ $7 + 1\frac{7}{12} = \underline{8\frac{7}{12}}$

$2\frac{1}{4} + 1\frac{1}{2} + 4\frac{5}{6} = \underline{8\frac{7}{12}}$

---

1. $3\frac{2}{3} + 2\frac{1}{2} + 2\frac{1}{4}$

   a. What is the smallest number divisible by 3, 2, and 4? __12__

   b. Write each fraction as an equivalent fraction with the least common denominator. $\frac{2}{3} = \frac{8}{12}, \frac{1}{2} = \frac{6}{12}, \frac{1}{4} = \frac{3}{12}$

   c. Now add the fractions. What is the sum of the fractions? __$\frac{17}{12}$__

   d. Simplify the sum. __$1\frac{5}{12}$__   **e.** $3\frac{2}{3} + 2\frac{1}{2} + 2\frac{1}{4} =$ __$8\frac{5}{12}$__

2. $1\frac{1}{8} + 2\frac{3}{4} + 3\frac{1}{2} =$ __$7\frac{3}{8}$__   **3.** $6\frac{5}{6} + 4\frac{1}{8} + 5\frac{2}{3} =$ __$16\frac{5}{8}$__

Name _____

Subtracting Mixed Numbers
Example 1 Find $3\frac{1}{8} - 1\frac{1}{2}$.

First, change the fractions so they all have the same denominator.

Find a number that is divisible by both denominators. This number is the common denominator.

The denominators are 8 and 2. 8 is divisible by 8 and 2, so 8 is the common denominator.

Write each fraction as an equivalent fraction with the least common denominator.

$\frac{1}{8} = \frac{1}{8}$ $\frac{1}{2} = \frac{?}{8}$ $\frac{1 \times 4}{2 \times 4} = \frac{4}{8}$ $3\frac{1}{8}$
                                       $- 1\frac{4}{8}$

Since you can not take away $\frac{4}{8}$ from $\frac{1}{8}$, regroup.

$1 = \frac{8}{8}$ $\frac{8}{8} + \frac{1}{8} = \frac{9}{8}$ $3\frac{1}{8} \longrightarrow 2\frac{9}{8}$
                              $- 1\frac{1}{2} \longrightarrow - 1\frac{4}{8}$
                                    $1\frac{5}{8}$ So, $3\frac{1}{8} - 1\frac{1}{2} = 1\frac{5}{8}$.

Example 2 Find $4 - 2\frac{3}{4}$.

Since there is no fraction from which to subtract $\frac{3}{4}$, regroup.

    4 $1 = \frac{4}{4} \longrightarrow 3\frac{4}{4}$
$- 2\frac{3}{4}$ $\longrightarrow - 2\frac{3}{4}$ So, $4 - 2\frac{3}{4} = 1\frac{1}{4}$.
                                    $1\frac{1}{4}$

---

1. $6\frac{1}{3} - 2\frac{4}{9}$

   a. What number is divisible by 3 and 9? __9__

   b. Subtract the fractions. Did you need to regroup? __yes__

   c. $6\frac{1}{3} - 2\frac{4}{9} =$ __$3\frac{8}{9}$__

2. $7 - 2\frac{2}{5} =$ __$4\frac{3}{5}$__   **3.** $4\frac{4}{5} - 2\frac{1}{2} =$ __$2\frac{3}{10}$__   **4.** $5 - 1\frac{1}{2} =$ __$3\frac{1}{2}$__

Compare Strategies: Work Backward/Draw a Picture

The scouts worked at a car wash to raise money. They raised twice as much money on Saturday as they did on Friday. On Sunday, they earned three times what they earned on Saturday. On Friday, they had earned $86. What did they earn on Saturday? on Sunday?

You know that the scouts earned $86 on Friday. You can draw a picture and work backward to find out how much they earned on Saturday and Sunday.

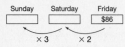

Sunday   Saturday   Friday
                            $86

× 3   × 2

Find the amount earned on Saturday. 2 × $86 = $172, so they earned $172 on Saturday. Write $172 in the box for Saturday above.

Find the amount earned on Sunday. 3 × $172 = $516, so they earned $516 on Sunday. Write $516 in the box for Sunday above.

The scouts earned $172 on Saturday and $516 on Sunday.

Work backward from an answer to solve the problem.

1. Lin rode his bike to the store. He rode twice as long on Cherry Lane as he did on 1st St. He rode 0.2 mi more on 1st St. than on Jay Rd. Lin rode his bike 0.8 mi on Jay Rd. How far did Lin ride his bike to the store?

   a. Draw boxes and arrows to show how you will work backward.

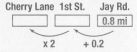

   Cherry Lane   1st St.   Jay Rd.
                              0.8 mi

   × 2   + 0.2

   b. How far did Lin ride his bike on each street?

   Jay Rd.—0.8 mi, 1st St.—1.0 mi, Cherry Lane—2.0 mi

   c. How far did Lin ride to the store? 3.8 mi

Linear Measure

Measure the model car to the nearest $\frac{1}{2}$-inch. It is between $2\frac{1}{2}$ and 3 in. long. It is closer to $2\frac{1}{2}$ than 3 in., so the car measures $2\frac{1}{2}$ in. to the nearest $\frac{1}{2}$-inch.

1. Measure the car to the nearest $\frac{1}{4}$-inch.
   a. The car is between $2\frac{1}{2}$ and $2\frac{3}{4}$ in. long.
   b. The car measures $2\frac{3}{4}$ in. to the nearest $\frac{1}{4}$-inch.

2. Measure the car to the nearest $\frac{1}{8}$-inch.
   a. The car is between $2\frac{5}{8}$ and $2\frac{3}{4}$ in. long.
   b. The car measures $2\frac{5}{8}$ in. to the nearest $\frac{1}{8}$-inch.

Find the length to the nearest $\frac{1}{4}$-inch.

3. $1\frac{1}{4}$ in. _____

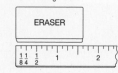

Find the length to the nearest $\frac{1}{8}$-inch.

4. $1\frac{5}{8}$ in. _____

ERASER

Feet, Yards, and Miles

Example 1   27 inches = _____ feet _____ inches

Use cubes to help you find the answer.

12 inches = 1 foot. If each cube in 1 inch long, 12 cubes = 1 foot.

Line up 27 cubes in groups of 12 cubes to show feet.

12 cubes   12 cubes

1 ft   1 ft   3 in.

How many groups of 12 do you have? 2

How many cubes are left over? 3

So, 27 inches = 2 feet 3 inches

Example 2   2 yards 2 feet = _____ feet

Use addition to help you find the answer. 1 yard = 3 feet

1 yard ⟶ 3 feet
1 yard ⟶ 3 feet
+ 2 feet ⟶ 2 feet
        8 feet   So, 2 yards 2 feet = 8 feet

---

1. 22 feet = _____ yd _____ ft
   a. Use cubes. If each cube represents 1 foot, how many cubes would equal 1 yard? 3
   b. Draw cubes in the space below to show yards and feet.
   ▢▢▢ ▢▢▢ ▢▢▢ ▢▢▢ ▢▢▢ ▢▢▢ ▢▢▢ ▢
   c. 22 feet = 7 yd 1 ft

2. 4 feet 4 inches = _____ in.
   a. Use addition. Write the number sentence you would use.
   12 + 12 + 12 + 12 + 4 = 52
   b. 4 feet 4 inches = 52 in.

3. 31 in. = 2 ft 7 in.   4. 5 yd 1 ft = 16 ft

Analyze Word Problems: Exact or Estimate?

Derek walks his dog for 30 minutes every evening after doing dishes. Derek's family has dinner at about 6:30 P.M. The family usually finishes eating in about 40 minutes. The dishes usually ake about 15 minutes. About what time does Derek walk the dog?

Hint: When a problem uses words such as "about," this usually means an estimate is close enough.

What do you know?   Dinner is around 6:30 P.M.

Eating takes about 40 min.

Dishes take about 15 min.

40 min and 15 min is about 1 hour.

Derek walks his dog at about 7:30 P.M.

Decide whether you need an estimate or exact answer. Solve.

1. Laura needs to read 30 more pages for homework, which will take about 20 minutes, after dinner. She wants to do this before walking the dog. Laura finished eating at 5:30. About what time will she be able to walk the dog?

   estimate; 5:45 to 6:00

2. Your mom sent you to the grocery store to buy some bread and milk, which cost $3.45. You give the clerk a $5.00 bill. How much change should you receive?

   exact; $1.55

3. You earn $10 each day you help at the animal clinic. You want to buy 2 CD's that cost $19.95 each. How many days will you have to work to earn the money for the CD's?

   estimate; 4 days

Exploring Multiplication of Whole Numbers by Fractions

In your book you multiplied whole numbers by fractions using counters. Here is another way to multiply by fractions.

Find $\frac{1}{3}$ of 9.

Draw 9 squares. Divide them into 3 equal groups. One of the groups shows $\frac{1}{3}$ of 9. There are __3__ squares in each group, so $\frac{1}{3}$ of 9 is __3__.

Find $\frac{2}{5}$ of 10.

Draw 10 squares. Divide them into 5 equal groups. One of the groups shows $\frac{1}{5}$ of 10, so 2 groups show $\frac{2}{5}$ of 10. There are __2__ squares in each group, so $\frac{2}{5}$ of 10 = 2 × 2 = __4__.

1. Find $\frac{1}{4}$ of 8
   a. Draw 8 squares.
   b. Divide the squares into 4 equal groups.
   c. How many squares are in each group? __2__
   d. $\frac{1}{4}$ of 8 is __2__

2. Find $\frac{2}{3}$ of 9
   a. Draw 9 squares.
   b. Divide the squares into 3 equal groups.
   c. How many squares are in each group? __3__
   d. $\frac{2}{3}$ of 9 is __6__

3. $\frac{1}{6}$ of 12 is __2__
4. $\frac{3}{5}$ of 15 is __9__
5. $\frac{3}{8}$ of 16 is __6__
6. $\frac{1}{9}$ of 27 is __3__

Multiplying with Fractions

You can use the numerator and denominator of fractions to help you multiply a whole number by a fraction. This table gives an example. Fill in the missing information to see how the table works.

Steps	$\frac{1}{5}$ of 15	$\frac{2}{5}$ of 15	$\frac{3}{5}$ of 15	$\frac{4}{5}$ of 15
What is the denominator?	5	5	5	5
Divide whole number by the denominator.	15 ÷ 5	15 ÷ 5	15 ÷ 5	15 ÷ 5
Quotient	3	3	3	3
What is the numerator?	1	2	3	4
Multiply numerator by the answer above.	1 × 3	2 × 3	3 × 3	4 × 3
Product	3	6	9	12

Find each product. Follow the steps above. Use mental math.

1. $\frac{1}{5}$ of 20 __4__
2. $\frac{1}{4}$ of 24 __6__
3. $\frac{1}{3}$ of 18 __6__

4. $\frac{1}{10}$ of 30 __3__
5. $\frac{1}{6}$ of 12 __2__
6. $\frac{3}{5}$ of 10 __6__

7. $\frac{2}{5}$ of 20 __8__
8. $\frac{3}{4}$ of 24 __18__
9. $\frac{2}{3}$ of 18 __12__

10. $\frac{1}{7}$ of 28 __4__
11. $\frac{1}{9}$ of 27 __3__
12. $\frac{3}{8}$ of 32 __12__

Estimating Products

Fill in the chart below to see how different methods of estimating products of fractions work.

METHOD	EXAMPLES	THINK
Round to the nearest whole number.	$1\frac{4}{5} \times 7$	• $1\frac{4}{5}$ is near 2 • 2 × 7 = 14 • estimate: 14
	$3\frac{7}{8} \times 8$	• $3\frac{7}{8}$ is near 4 • 4 × 8 = 32 • estimate: 32
Use compatible numbers (numbers that divide evenly).	$\frac{1}{4} \times 25$	• 4 goes evenly into 24. • $\frac{1}{4} \times 24 = 6$ • estimate: 6
	$\frac{2}{7} \times 48$	• 7 goes evenly into 49 • $\frac{2}{7} \times 49 = (49 ÷ 7) \times 2 = 14$ • estimate: 14
Replace the fraction with a benchmark.	$\frac{3}{8} \times 20$	• $\frac{3}{8}$ is near $\frac{4}{8}$, or $\frac{1}{2}$. • $\frac{1}{2} \times 20 = 10$ • estimate: 10
	$\frac{4}{9} \times 20$	• $\frac{4}{9}$ is near $\frac{1}{2}$ • $\frac{1}{2} \times 20 = 10$ • estimate: 10

Estimate each product.

1. $\frac{1}{5} \times 31$ __6__
2. $\frac{7}{9} \times 10$ __7__
3. $\frac{1}{6} \times 43$ __7__
4. $\frac{6}{11} \times 20$ __10__

Exploring Multiplication of Fractions by Fractions

In your book, you found fractions of fractions by folding paper. Here is another way to multiply fractions by fractions.

Step 1 To find $\frac{1}{2}$ of $\frac{1}{3}$, start with a rectangle.

Step 2 Divide the rectangle into 3 parts. Each part is $\frac{1}{3}$. Lightly shade $\frac{1}{3}$.

Step 3 Divide the rectangle in half horizontally. Shade $\frac{1}{2}$ of the rectangle. Now there are 6 parts. Each part is $\frac{1}{6}$.

Step 4 Count the sections that were shaded twice. One out of the 6 sections was shaded twice. So, $\frac{1}{2}$ of $\frac{1}{3}$ is $\frac{1}{6}$.

Use the drawing to help you find $\frac{1}{4}$ of $\frac{1}{2}$.

1. Divide the rectangle into 2 parts.
   Shade 1 part.
   Each part is $\frac{1}{2}$.

2. Divide the rectangle into fourths.
   Shade $\frac{1}{4}$.
   Each part is $\frac{1}{8}$.
   $\frac{1}{4}$ of $\frac{1}{2}$ is $\frac{1}{8}$.

Multiplying Fractions

Common factors can help you multiply fractions by fractions.

Think about these fractions. Can you simplify them?

$\frac{4}{10}$ $\frac{2}{8}$

- To simplify fractions, factor each numerator and denominator.

$\frac{4}{10} = \frac{2 \times 2}{2 \times 5}$ $\frac{2}{8} = \frac{2 \times 1}{2 \times 4}$

- Then divide by common factors.

$\frac{4}{10} = \frac{\cancel{2} \times 2}{\cancel{2} \times 5} = \frac{2}{5}$ $\frac{2}{8} = \frac{\cancel{2} \times 1}{\cancel{2} \times 4} = \frac{1}{4}$

When you multiply fractions, you can use the same method of dividing common factors.

Find $\frac{1}{4} \times \frac{4}{5}$. The common factor is 4.

$\frac{1}{4} \times \frac{4}{5} = \frac{\cancel{4} \times 1}{\cancel{4} \times 5} = \frac{1}{5}$

Simplify the fractions.

1. $\frac{6}{8} = \frac{2 \times 3}{2 \times 4} = \underline{\frac{3}{4}}$ 2. $\frac{5}{10} = \frac{5 \times 1}{5 \times 2} = \underline{\frac{1}{2}}$

Find the product. Simplify.

3. $\frac{3}{8} \times \frac{1}{3} = \frac{3 \times 1}{3 \times 8} = \underline{\frac{1}{8}}$ 4. $\frac{1}{2} \times \frac{4}{5} = \frac{4 \times 1}{2 \times 5} = \frac{4}{10} = \underline{\frac{2}{5}}$

5. $\frac{2}{10} \times \frac{3}{5} = \underline{\frac{3}{25}}$ 6. $\frac{6}{8} \times \frac{2}{10} = \underline{\frac{3}{20}}$

7. $\frac{4}{4} \times \frac{5}{16} = \underline{\frac{5}{16}}$ 8. $\frac{2}{6} \times \frac{6}{12} = \underline{\frac{1}{6}}$

9. $\frac{5}{10} \times \frac{3}{5} = \underline{\frac{3}{10}}$ 10. $\frac{2}{3} \times \frac{3}{11} = \underline{\frac{2}{11}}$

Analyze Word Problems:
Overestimating and Underestimating

Terence has $4.45 in his pocket, $7.93 at home, and $2.19 in his desk. Can he buy a $10.95 book with the total amount of money?

Terence wants to be sure he has enough money. If he rounds each amount to higher dollar amounts, his estimate will be greater than the actual amount he has.

Terence should underestimate.

Round each amount to a lesser dollar amount.

$4.45 is close to $4.00

$7.95 is close to $7.00

$2.19 is close to __$2.00__.

Add the three rounded dollar amounts.

__$4.00__ + __$7.00__ + __$2.00__ = __$13.00__

Since all the dollar amounts were lowered, Terence has at least $13.00. So, he can buy a book for $10.95

Karol must earn 500 points in order to receive an A in math class. She has earned the following points so far—85, 92, 79, 99, and 87. She has one more project. If she earns 50 points, will she receive an A?

1. Should you overestimate or underestimate to solve the problem? Why?

   Underestimate; Karol wants to be sure that 50 points is enough to earn her an A.

2. Write the rounded amounts. __80, 90, 70, 90, 80__

3. About how many points has Karol earned so far? __410 points__

4. Will 50 points be enough for Karol to get an A? Explain.

   No, Karol needs more than 50 points.

Multiplying Whole Numbers
by Fractions

Multiply $\frac{1}{4}$ and 3.

One way to solve the problem is to draw a picture.

Shade in $\frac{1}{4}$ three times.

$\frac{1}{4} + \frac{1}{4} + \frac{1}{4} = \frac{3}{4}$

$\frac{1}{4} \times 3 = \frac{3 \times 1}{4} = \frac{3}{4}$

Find each product. Draw a picture to help.

1. $\frac{3}{8} \times 3 = \underline{1\frac{1}{8}}$

2. $\frac{4}{9} \times 2 = \underline{\frac{8}{9}}$

3. $\frac{7}{8} \times 4 = \underline{3\frac{1}{2}}$ 4. $\frac{1}{3} \times 9 = \underline{3}$

5. $\frac{1}{6} \times 9 = \underline{1\frac{1}{2}}$ 6. $\frac{3}{7} \times 12 = \underline{5\frac{1}{7}}$

7. $\frac{3}{4} \times 6 = \underline{4\frac{1}{2}}$ 8. $\frac{2}{5} \times 8 = \underline{3\frac{1}{5}}$

9. $\frac{5}{6} \times 5 = \underline{4\frac{1}{6}}$ 10. $\frac{3}{10} \times 7 = \underline{2\frac{1}{10}}$

11. $\frac{2}{3} \times 4 = \underline{2\frac{2}{3}}$ 12. $\frac{1}{6} \times 18 = \underline{3}$

13. $\frac{4}{7} \times 11 = \underline{6\frac{2}{7}}$ 14. $\frac{5}{8} \times 12 = \underline{7\frac{1}{2}}$

15. $\frac{2}{9} \times 7 = \underline{1\frac{5}{9}}$ 16. $\frac{3}{11} \times 9 = \underline{2\frac{5}{11}}$

17. $\frac{5}{12} \times 4 = \underline{1\frac{2}{3}}$ 18. $\frac{3}{4} \times 10 = \underline{7\frac{1}{2}}$

Multiplying Whole Numbers
and Mixed Numbers

Step 1   Rewrite. Whole number × denominator + numerator. Write this number over the denominator and remember that the denominator does not change.

$2\frac{3}{4} \times 2\frac{2}{3} = \frac{11}{4} \times \frac{8}{3}$

Step 2   Simplify. Divide by common factors.

$\frac{11}{\cancel{4}_1} \times \frac{\cancel{8}^2}{3}$

Step 3   Multiply. Rewrite an improper fraction as a mixed number if necessary.

$\frac{11}{1} \times \frac{2}{3} = \frac{22}{3}$ $22 \div 3 = \underline{7\ R1}$, so $\frac{22}{3} = 7\frac{1}{3}$

Follow the steps to find each product and complete the table.

		Step 1: Rewrite	Step 2: Simplify Factors	Step 3: Multiply
1.	$3\frac{1}{3} \times 6$	$\frac{10}{3} \times 6$	$\frac{10}{\cancel{3}_1} \times \frac{\cancel{6}^2}{1}$	$10 \times 2 = 20$
2.	$1\frac{3}{4} \times 2$	$\frac{7}{4} \times 2$	$\frac{7}{\cancel{4}_2} \times \frac{\cancel{2}^1}{1}$	$\frac{7}{2} \times 1 = \frac{7}{2} = 3\frac{1}{2}$
3.	$8\frac{2}{3} \times 4$	$\frac{26}{3} \times 4$	$\frac{26}{3} \times \frac{4}{1}$	$\frac{26}{3} \times 4 = \frac{104}{3} = 34\frac{2}{3}$
4.	$1\frac{1}{9} \times 3$	$\frac{10}{9} \times 3$	$\frac{10}{\cancel{9}_3} \times \frac{\cancel{3}^1}{1}$	$\frac{10}{3} \times 1 = \frac{10}{3} = 3\frac{1}{3}$
5.	$2\frac{1}{2} \times 8$	$\frac{5}{2} \times 8$	$\frac{5}{\cancel{2}_1} \times \frac{\cancel{8}^4}{1}$	$\frac{5}{1} \times 4 = 20$
6.	$1\frac{1}{2} \times 3\frac{2}{9}$	$\frac{3}{2} \times \frac{29}{9}$	$\frac{\cancel{3}^1}{2} \times \frac{29}{\cancel{9}_3}$	$\frac{1}{2} \times \frac{29}{3} = \frac{29}{6} = 4$
7.	$8\frac{1}{4} \times 7\frac{1}{3}$	$\frac{33}{4} \times \frac{22}{3}$	$\frac{\cancel{33}^{11}}{4} \times \frac{22}{\cancel{3}_1}$	$\frac{11}{4} \times \frac{11}{1} = \frac{121}{4} = 60\frac{1}{4}$
8.	$4\frac{3}{4} \times 3\frac{1}{5}$	$\frac{19}{4} \times \frac{16}{5}$	$\frac{19}{\cancel{4}_1} \times \frac{\cancel{16}^4}{5}$	$\frac{19}{1} \times \frac{4}{5} = \frac{76}{5} = 15\frac{1}{5}$
9.	$5\frac{1}{2} \times 2\frac{2}{3}$	$\frac{11}{2} \times \frac{8}{3}$	$\frac{11}{\cancel{2}_1} \times \frac{\cancel{8}^4}{3}$	$\frac{11}{1} \times \frac{4}{3} = \frac{44}{3} = 14\frac{2}{3}$
10.	$6\frac{3}{5} \times 1\frac{7}{8}$	$\frac{33}{5} \times \frac{15}{8}$	$\frac{33}{\cancel{5}_1} \times \frac{\cancel{15}^3}{8}$	$\frac{33}{1} \times \frac{3}{8} = \frac{99}{8} = 12\frac{3}{8}$

Panel 1 (top left)

Name _____

**Another Look
9-9**

Compare Strategies:
Logical Reasoning/Draw a Picture

Sergie, Alexia, Michael, and Sophie are waiting in line for movie tickets. Sergie is neither first nor last. Sophie stands behind Alexis, but Sophie is not last. Alexis is not second and Sophie is not third. Michael is either first or last

From the information above, a table can be filled in as to the right. Use logical reasoning to complete the rest of the table.

	Sergei	Alexis	Michael	Sophie
1st	no	yes	no	no
2nd	no	no	no	yes
3rd	yes	no	no	no
4th	no	no	yes	no

1. How do you know that Alexis never can be last and Sophie never can be first?

because Alexis is in front of Sophie

2. In what order are they in line? Would drawing a picture help to answer this problem?

Alexis, Sophie, Sergei, Michael; Possible answer: Yes, because it would be easier to see who stands next to each other.

3. Jan, Charlie, Alison, and Victoria each ordered a different sandwich. Their orders were turkey, veggie burger, salami, and cheese. No one ordered a sandwich that had the same number of syllables as his or her name. Alison avoids dairy products and did not order the veggie burger. Victoria and Charlie do not like salami. Who ordered which sandwich?

Make a table. Use the clues to fill in the table.

	Jan	Charlie	Alison	Victoria
Turkey	X	X	*	X
Veggie Burger	X	*	X	X
Salami	*	X	X	X
Cheese	X	X	X	*

Use with pages 426–427. **121**

Panel 2 (top right)

Name _____

**Another Look
9-10**

Exploring Division of Fractions

In your book, you used fraction strips to divide whole numbers by fractions. Here is another way to divide by a fraction.

If you wanted to divide 4 into $\frac{1}{6}$'s, you could draw it like this:

The drawing helps you to see that $4 \div \frac{1}{6} =$ __24__.

Find each quotient. Draw a picture to help.

1. $4 \div \frac{1}{3} =$ __12__

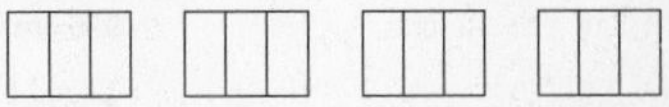

2. $6 \div \frac{1}{6} =$ __36__

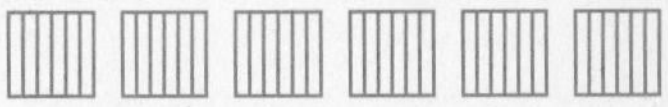

3. $5 \div \frac{1}{8} =$ __40__

4. $7 \div \frac{1}{4} =$ __28__

5. $8 \div \frac{1}{2} =$ __16__

122 Use with pages 428–429.

Panel 3 (bottom left)

Name _____

**Another Look
10-1**

Exploring Estimating and Measuring Length

In your book you chose appropriate units of measurement to estimate length and height of various items. Here is another way to explore length.

Suppose your friend told you that the distance between the swings and the slide at the park was 10 km. Follow these steps to decide if this is reasonable.

Step 1 Think: How far is 1 km? In your book you learned that four city blocks are about 1 km long. It would probably take you about 10 minutes to walk 1 km. How long would it take to walk 10 km?
__100 min or 1 hr 40 min__

Step 2 Visualize: Picture yourself walking from the swings to the slide at the park. How long would it take?
__Possible answer: 10 to 15 sec__

Step 3 Decide: Is it reasonable that the swings and the slide would be 10 km apart, even in a large park?
__no__

Decide if each statement is reasonable. Write yes or no.

1. Marcie said that she saw a butterfly that was 1 m long. __no__

2. Dion said that he caught a fish that was 2 cm long, and it fed his whole family. __no__

3. Claire said that her parrot had a wingspan of 1 km. __no__

4. Joyce's dictionary is 5 cm thick. __yes__

5. Keesha's dining room table is 2 m long. __yes__

6. Pablo lives 50 km from his aunt's house. He can walk there in about an hour. __no__

7. The caboose on a train is 1 dm long. __no__

Use with pages 440–441. **123**

Panel 4 (bottom right)

Name _____

**Another Look
10-2**

Millimeters

Use the following chart to help you know how many times to multiply or divide by 10 when converting metric units:

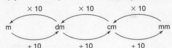

When moving from larger to smaller units, multiply by 10.

4 m = ▨ cm

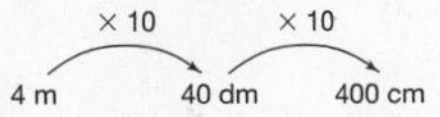

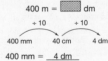

4 m = __400 cm__

When moving from smaller to larger units, divide by 10.

400 m = ▨ dm

400 mm = __4 dm__

In the space below each problem, show how you multiplied or divided by 10 to change each metric unit.

1. 7 m = __70__ dm
$7 \times 10 = 70$

2. 70 mm = __7__ cm
$70 \div 10 = 7$

3. 80 m = __8,000__ cm
$80 \times 10 \times 10 = 8,000$

4. 800 m = __8,000__ dm
$800 \times 10 = 8,000$

5. 8,000 mm = __8__ m
$8,000 \div 10 \div 10 \div 10 = 8$

6. 80 m = __80,000__ mm
$80 \times 10 \times 10 \times 10 = 80,000$

7. 1,500 cm = __15__ m
$1,500 \div 10 \div 10 = 15$

8. 150 m = __150,000__ mm
$150 \times 10 \times 10 \times 10 = 150,000$

124 Use with pages 442–443.

Name _____

Centimeters, Meters, and Decimals

Use the diagram to change
from m to cm and from cm to m.

× 100

m → cm

÷ 100

7 m = [ ] cm   85 cm = [ ] m

7 × 100 = 700   85 ÷ 100 = 0.85

7 m = __700__ cm   85 cm = __0.85__ m

_____

Complete.

1. 8 m = [ ] cm   **2.** 976 cm = [ ] m

   a. 8 [×] 100 = __800__   **a.** 976 [÷] 100 = __9.76__

   b. 8 m = __800__ cm   **b.** 976 cm = __9.76__ m

3. 4 cm = __0.04__ m   **4.** 800 m = __80,000__ cm

5. 2.16 m = __216__ cm   **6.** 90.8 m = __9,080__ cm

7. 1,882 cm = __18.82__ m   **8.** 90,000 cm = __900__ m

Name _____

Millimeters, Centimeters, and Decimals

The following diagram shows how to change between
cm and mm and between m and cm.

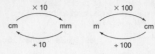

× 10   × 100

cm → mm   m → cm

÷ 10   ÷ 100

76 mm = [ ] cm   7 m = [ ] cm

76 ÷ 10 = 7.6   7 × 100 = 700

76 mm = __7.6__ cm   7 m = __700__ cm

_____

Complete.

1. 80 m = [ ] cm   **2.** 976 mm = [ ] cm

   a. 80 [×] 100 = __8,000__   **a.** 976 [÷] 10 = __97.6__

   b. 80 m = __8,000__ cm   **b.** 976 mm = __97.6__ cm

3. 14 cm = __0.14__ m   **4.** 19.87 m = __1,987__ cm

5. 8.32 m = __832__ cm   **6.** 1,437 mm = __143.7__ cm

7. 82 cm = __820__ mm   **8.** 7,321 cm = __73,210__ mm

Name _____

Exploring Perimeter of Polygons

In your book you explored perimeter by measuring shapes.
Here is another way to explore perimeter.

You can use grid paper to help you
find the perimeter of a polygon.

├─ 7 units ─┤

4 units

Count the number of units on each side
of the polygon. Then add.

4 units + 7 units + 4 units + 7 units = __22__ units

The perimeter is __22__ units.

This is a regular polygon. Each side is the
same length. Add the lengths of each side.

8 m + 8 m + 8 m = __24__

The perimeter is __24__ m.

8 m

_____

Find each perimeter.

1.

2.

__28 units__   __20 units__

3. 5 yd 3 yd   **4.**
   7 yd

7 dm

__15 yd__   __35 dm__

Name _____

Exploring Perimeter of Rectangles

In your book you used tables to explore perimeter. Here is
another way to understand perimeter. You can find the
perimeter of a rectangle by adding the lengths of each side.

You can also use a shortcut to find the perimeter of a
rectangle. Just add the length and the width. Then multiply
the sum by 2.

4 + 3 = 7

7 × 2 = 14   3 ft

The perimeter is 14 ft.   4 ft

_____

Find the perimeter of each rectangle.

1. a. l = __6 in.__

   b. w = __2 in.__   2 in.
                       6 in.

   c. __6__ + __2__ = __8__

   d. __8__ × 2 = __16__

   e. The perimeter is __16__ in.

2. 1 m   **3.** 2 cm
  6 m   7 cm

__14 m__   __18 cm__

4. 4 yd   **5.** 6 in.
  5 yd   16 in.

__18 yd__   __44 in.__

Exploring Area of Triangles

In your book you explored area of triangles by drawing triangles inside rectangles. Here is another way to find the area of triangles.

Use grid paper and the steps below to help you find the area of triangles.

10 units

6 units

Step 1 Count the number of units in the base and in the height.

base = __6__ units

Step 2 Find the product of the base and the height. Then divide by 2.

height = __10__ units

$6 \times 10 = 60$ $60 \div 2 = 30$

The area of the triangle is __30 units^2__.

Follow the same steps to find the area of each triangle:

1. a. Count the number of units in the base and in the height.

base = __3__ units   height = __8__ units

b. __3__ × __8__ = __24__

c. __24__ ÷ 2 = __12__

d. A = __12__ units^2

2. a. Count the number of units in the base and in the height.

base = __8__ units   height = __5__ units

b. __8__ × __5__ = __40__

c. __40__ ÷ 2 = __20__

d. A = __20__ units^2

Exploring Area of Other Polygons

In your book you used geoboards and dot paper to explore area of polygons. Here is another way. You can use grid paper to help you find area. Follow these steps.

Step 1 Draw lines to divide the polygon into rectangles and triangles. Shade in rectangles. Count the squares to find the area of each rectangle.

In this polygon, there is one rectangle. Its area is 12 square units.

Step 2 Extend the sides of each triangle into a rectangle. Count the squares in each new rectangle and divide by 2 to find the area of each triangle.

In this polygon, there is one triangle. Its area is 12 square units.

Step 3 Add the areas of the rectangle and triangle to find the area of the polygon.

$12 + 12 =$ __24 square units__

Follow the same steps to find the area of each polygon.

1.

__31 $\frac{1}{2}$__ square units

2.

__31__ square units

3.

__12__ square units

4.

__46 $\frac{1}{2}$__ square units

Exploring Area of Parallelograms

In your book you used cutouts and grid paper to explore area of parallelograms. Here is another way to find the area of a parallelogram using dot paper.

Step 1 Call the lower left dot of the parallelogram 0. Count the dots from left to right. The base of the parallelogram is 3 units.

0 1 2 3

Step 2 Draw a vertical line joining the dots in the middle of the parallelogram. Call the bottom dot 0, and count the dots from bottom to top. The height of the parallelogram is 2 units.

Step 3 Multiply the number of units in the base and the height to find the area.

3 units × 2 units = 6 square units or 6 units^2.

The area of the parallelogram is __6 units^2__.

Follow the steps to find the area of each parallelogram.

1.

__20__ units^2

2.

__30__ units^2

3.

__28__ units^2

4.

__18__ units^2

Exploring Algebra: Balancing Equations

In your book you explored balancing equations by using envelopes and counters. Here is another way to balance equations. Use a balance scale.

Count the marbles on the left side of the balance scale. Count the marbles showing on the right side. You do not know how many marbles are in the bag. Use n to represent the marbles in the bag. Write the problem as an equation.

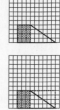

$16 = 8 + n$

To make the scales balance, there must be the same number of marbles on each side of the scale. For there to be 16 marbles on the right side, the bag must hold 8 marbles.

$16 = 8 +$ __8__

$n =$ __8__

Find the number of marbles in each marble bag.

1.

equation: __12 = 8 + n__

$n =$ __4__

2.

equation: __3 + n = 7__

$n =$ __4__

3.

equation: __5 = 2 + n__

$n =$ __3__

4.

equation: __4 + n = 15__

$n =$ __11__

Converting Units to Find Perimeter

Find the perimeter of the rectangle.

Step 1 Change feet to inches. 1 ft = 12 in.
Multiply the number of feet by 12. Add
the number of inches to the result.

1 ft 2 in.
2 ft 6 in.

2 ft 6 in. = (2 × 12) + 6 = 24 + 6 = __30 in.__
1 ft 2 in. = (1 × 12) + 2 = 12 + 2 = __14 in.__

Step 2 Add length and width and multiply by 2.

(30 + 14) × 2 = 44 × 2 = __88 in.__

Step 3 Convert the answer to larger units.
Change 88 in. to feet by dividing by 12.

88 ÷ 12 = __7 R4__
The remainder amount is the number of inches
left over. So 88 in. = __7 ft 4 in.__

Find the length, width, and perimeter of each rectangle in
inches. Then convert the answer to feet.

1.
6 ft 9 in.
8 ft 2 in.

a. length: __98 in.__

b. width: __81 in.__

c. perimeter: __358 in.__

d. perimeter in feet and inches:
__29 ft 10 in.__

2.
4 ft 8 in.
6 ft 7 in.

a. length: __79 in.__

b. width: __56 in.__

c. perimeter: __270 in.__

d. perimeter in feet and inches:
__22 ft 6 in.__

3.
2 ft 1 in.
5 ft 4 in.

a. perimeter in inches: __178 in.__

b. perimeter in feet and inches:
__14 ft 10 in.__

4.
3 ft 7 in.
5 ft 8 in.

a. perimeter in inches: __222 in.__

b. perimeter in feet and inches:
__18 ft 6 in.__

Exploring Area of Rectangles

In your book you drew gardens to find area. Here is another
way to find area.

You can find the area of a rectangle by using
grid paper and counting the square units inside
the rectangle.

There are 20 squares inside the rectangle.
So, the area of the rectangle is 20 square units.

Area = 20 square units or __20 units^2__

You can also find the area of a rectangle
by multiplying the length by the width.

3 ft
7 ft

length = 7 ft

width = 3 ft

Area = __7 ft × 3 ft__ = __21 ft^2__

Find the area of each rectangle.

1.
__12 units^2__

2.
__14 units^2__

3.
3 mm
6 mm
__18 mm^2__

4.
7 ft
9 ft
__63 ft^2__

5.
8 yd
13 yd
__104 yd^2__

6.
11 cm
17 cm
__187 cm^2__

Decision Making

Kim wants to join a club at her new school. There are
5 clubs she is interested in joining. All the clubs meet
after school.

Kim only has Monday and Wednesday afternoons free.
She wants to join a club with fewer than 40 members.

The table gives information about each club.

Club	Day the Club Meets	Number of Students
Drama	Wednesdays	42
Science	Wednesdays	70
Chess	Tuesdays	20
Computer	Mondays	43
Dance	Mondays	26

Since Kim can only join a club that meets on Monday or
Wednesday, she can't join the __chess club.__

Kim wants to join a club that has fewer than 40 members. Which club
has fewer than 40 members and meets on Monday or Wednesday?

__dance club__

1. What if Kim wanted to join a club that met on Mondays
that had more than 30 members? Which club could she join?
__computer club__

2. Suppose Terri could join a club that met on Tuesdays
or Thursdays. Which club could she join?
__chess club__

3. Pam has a friend in the dance club who gives her a ride
home after school. Which clubs could Pam join so that
she can get a ride home with her friend every day?

__computer club or dance club__

Exploring Area of Right Triangles

In your book you used the area of a rectangle to help you
find the area of a right triangle. Here is another way to find
the area of a right triangle.

You can use grid paper to help visualize the area.

4 units
4 units

You can find the area by counting the squares inside
the triangle. Put together the partial pieces to make
whole squares.

This triangle covers 8 squares on the grid paper, so its
area is 8 units^2.

Another way to find the area of a triangle is to multiply the
length of the base by the height. Then divide by 2.

4 × 4 = 16

16 ÷ 2 = 8

The area of the triangle is __8 units^2__.

Find the area of each right triangle.

1.
__4 units^2__

2.
__10 units^2__

3.
2 cm
7 cm
__7 cm^2__

4.
5 in.
5 in.
__12 $\frac{1}{2}$ in^2__

Name _____

Analyze Strategies: Look for a Pattern

Keesha had her hair cut on Jan. 1st. She had it cut again on Feb. 2nd and Mar. 6th. If this pattern continues, when will Keesha's next haircut be?

Use a calendar and make an organized list to look for a pattern in the numbers.

Month	Date
January	1
February	2
March	6

How many days after Jan. 1st is Feb. 2nd? __32__

How many days after Feb. 2nd is Mar. 6th? (Hint: It is not leap year.) __32__

The pattern is that Keesha has her hair cut every 32 days.

Keesha's next haircut will be 32 days after Mar. 6th, which is __Apr. 7th.__

1. When will Keesha's next 2 haircuts after April 7th be?
   __May 9th, June 10th__

Look for a pattern to help solve each problem.

2. On Monday, Skip called Lou at 9:00 A.M. On Tuesday, he called at 10:30 A.M. On Wednesday, he called at 12:00 noon. If this pattern continues, when will the next 2 phone calls be?
   Thursday at 1:30 P.M., Friday at 3:00 P.M.

3. While playing a game, Fiona took 1 step forward, 2 steps back, 2 steps forward, 2 steps back, 3 steps forward, 2 steps back. If this pattern continues, what will she do for the next 2 moves?
   __4 steps forward, 2 steps back__

Name _____

Exploring Circumference

In your book you used circles drawn with compasses to explore circumference. Here is another way to find circumference.

Find the dot in the center of the circle. Label it A.

Count the number of dots from the center to the edge of the circle. This number is the measure of the radius. In this circle, the radius measures __2 units.__

Multiply the radius by 2. Then multiply the product by π to find the circumference.

Use 3.14 for π.

$2 \times 2 =$ __4__ $4 \times 3.14 =$ __12.56__
The circumference is __12.56 units.__

Find the circumference of each circle.

1.
   a. The radius is __1__ unit(s).
   b. __1__ × 2 × 3.14 = __6.28__
   c. The circumference is __6.28__ units.

2.
   a. The radius is __3__ unit(s).
   b. __3__ × 2 × 3.14 = __18.84__
   c. The circumference is __18.84__ units.

3.
   a. The radius is __4__ unit(s).
   b. __4__ × 2 × 3.14 = __25.12__
   c. The circumference is __25.12__ units.

4.
   a. The radius is __5__ unit(s).
   b. __5__ × 2 × 3.14 = __31.4__
   c. The circumference is __31.4__ units.

Name _____

Exploring Solids

In your book you used Power Solids to explore prisms and pyramids. Here is another way to look at these solids.

A **pyramid** is a solid figure whose base is a polygon and whose faces are triangles. Here are some common pyramids.

Triangular pyramid   Rectangular pyramid   Pentagonal pyramid

A **prism** is a solid figure whose bases are congruent and whose faces are usually rectangles. Here are some common prisms.

Triangular prism   Rectangular prism   Pentagonal prism

Write the name of each solid.

1. __rectangular prism__

2. __triangular pyramid__

3. __pentagonal prism__

4. __pentagonal pyramid__

Name _____

Exploring Patterns with Solids

In your book you explored patterns by counting the faces, vertices, and edges of solids. Here is another way to understand patterns in solids.

Triangular pyramid — edge   Rectangular prism — edge

To find the number of edges in a pyramid, count the number of edges of the base and multiply by 2.

The triangular pyramid has a triangular base. Triangles have 3 sides. 3 × 2 = 6
So, the pyramid has 6 edges.

To find the number of faces in a pyramid, count the number of edges of the base and add 1.

The triangular pyramid has a triangular base. Triangles have 3 sides. 3 + 1 = 4
So, the pyramid has 4 faces.

To find the number of edges in a prism, count the number of edges of the base and multiply by 3.

The rectangular prism has a rectangular base. Rectangles have 4 edges. 4 × 3 = 12
So, the prism has 12 edges.

To find the number of faces in a prism, count the number of edges of the base and add 2.

The rectangular prism has a rectangular base. Rectangles have 4 sides. 4 + 2 = 6
So, the prism has 6 faces.

Find the number of edges and faces of each solid.

1.
   a. How many edges in the base? __3__
   b. How many edges in the prism? __9__
   c. How many faces? __5__

2.
   a. How many edges in the base? __4__
   b. How many edges in the pyramid? __8__
   c. How many faces? __5__

Exploring Nets

In your book you explored nets by drawing nets on dot paper. Here is another way to explore nets.

Trace and cut out the net. Fold it along the dotted lines.

Does this net make a cube?

yes

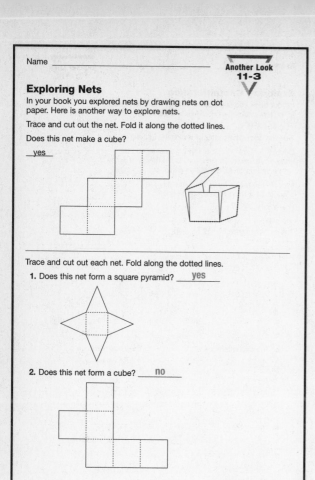

Trace and cut out each net. Fold along the dotted lines.

1. Does this net form a square pyramid? _____ yes

2. Does this net form a cube? _____ no

Exploring Surface Area

In your book you found the surface area of a solid by taking the figure apart and finding the area of each surface. Here is that method of finding surface area.

Find the area of each face.

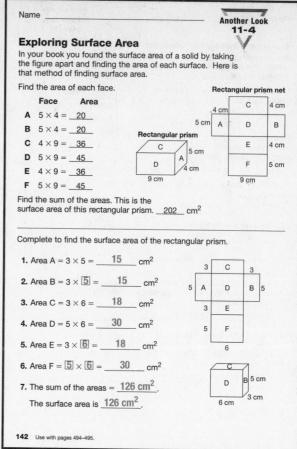

Rectangular prism net

Face		Area
A	$5 \times 4 =$	20
B	$5 \times 4 =$	20
C	$4 \times 9 =$	36
D	$5 \times 9 =$	45
E	$4 \times 9 =$	36
F	$5 \times 9 =$	45

Find the sum of the areas. This is the surface area of this rectangular prism. __202__ cm²

Complete to find the surface area of the rectangular prism.

1. Area A = 3 × 5 = ____15____ cm²

2. Area B = 3 × 5̄ = ____15____ cm²

3. Area C = 3 × 6 = ____18____ cm²

4. Area D = 5 × 6 = ____30____ cm²

5. Area E = 3 × 6̄ = ____18____ cm²

6. Area F = 5̄ × 6̄ = ____30____ cm²

7. The sum of the areas = __126 cm²__.

The surface area is __126 cm²__.

Decision Making

Solve.

1. The cost of wood is $10.00 per 8-ft board, or $1.50 for each foot when the board is less than 8 ft long. How much wood can you afford for:

a. $11? __8 ft__

b. $20? __16 ft__

c. $27.50? __21 ft__

d. $28? __21 ft__

2. Each board is 8 ft long. How many inches long is:

a. 1 board? __96 in.__

b. 2 boards? __192 in.__

c. two 8-ft boards + one 3-ft board? __228 in.__

3. Suppose you used 51 in. of wood from an 8-ft board. How many inches of wood would you have left? __45 in.__

4. Suppose you used 32 in. of wood from a 4-ft board. How many inches of wood would you have left? __16 in.__

5. Suppose you cut lengths of wood measuring 30 in., 21 in., 20 in., and 12 in. from an 8-ft board. Do you have enough wood left to cut another 20-in. length of wood? Explain.

No. You would only have 13 in. of wood left.

6. Suppose you cut lengths of wood measuring 16 in., 30 in., 11 in., and 13 in. from an 8-ft board. Do you have enough wood left to cut another 2-ft length of wood? Explain.

Yes. You would have 2 ft 2 in. of wood left.

Ounces, Pounds, and Tons

The ounce (oz), pound (lb), and ton (T) are customary units used to measure weight.

16 oz = 1 lb   2,000 lb = 1 T

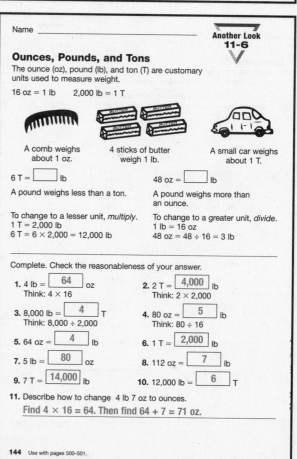

A comb weighs about 1 oz.

4 sticks of butter weigh 1 lb.

A small car weighs about 1 T.

6 T = [ ] lb
A pound weighs less than a ton.

48 oz = [ ] lb
A pound weighs more than an ounce.

To change to a lesser unit, *multiply*.
1 T = 2,000 lb
6 T = 6 × 2,000 = 12,000 lb

To change to a greater unit, *divide*.
1 lb = 16 oz
48 oz = 48 ÷ 16 = 3 lb

Complete. Check the reasonableness of your answer.

1. 4 lb = [64] oz
Think: 4 × 16

2. 2 T = [4,000] lb
Think: 2 × 2,000

3. 8,000 lb = [4] T
Think: 8,000 ÷ 2,000

4. 80 oz = [5] lb
Think: 80 ÷ 16

5. 64 oz = [4] lb

6. 1 T = [2,000] lb

7. 5 lb = [80] oz

8. 112 oz = [7] lb

9. 7 T = [14,000] lb

10. 12,000 lb = [6] T

11. Describe how to change 4 lb 7 oz to ounces.

Find 4 × 16 = 64. Then find 64 + 7 = 71 oz.

11-7 — Grams and Kilograms

Name _____

Another Look 11-7

Grams and Kilograms

The gram (g) and kilogram (kg) are metric units of mass. "Kilo" means one thousand, so 1 kilogram = 1,000 grams.

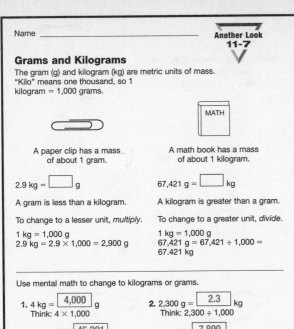

A paper clip has a mass of about 1 gram.

A math book has a mass of about 1 kilogram.

2.9 kg = [ ] g

A gram is less than a kilogram.

67,421 g = [ ] kg

A kilogram is greater than a gram.

To change to a lesser unit, *multiply*.

1 kg = 1,000 g
2.9 kg = 2.9 × 1,000 = 2,900 g

To change to a greater unit, *divide*.

1 kg = 1,000 g
67,421 g = 67,421 ÷ 1,000 = 67.421 kg

Use mental math to change to kilograms or grams.

1. 4 kg = [4,000] g
Think: 4 × 1,000

2. 2,300 g = [2.3] kg
Think: 2,300 ÷ 1,000

3. 45,201 g = [45.201] kg
Think: 45,201 ÷ 1,000

4. 7.8 kg = [7,800] g
Think: 7.8 × 1,000

5. 5.122 kg = [5,122] g

6. 0.567 kg = [567] g

7. 9,000 g = [9] kg

8. 78,000 g = [78] kg

9. 542 g = [0.542] kg

10. 50 kg = [50,000] g

Use with pages 502–503. **145**

11-8 — Temperature

Name _____

Another Look 11-8

Temperature

How do you calculate differences in temperature? It depends on where the temperatures fall.

If both temperatures are above or below 0°, <u>ignore any negatives</u> and subtract the lesser number from the greater one.

If one of the temperatures is above 0° and one is below 0°, <u>ignore the negative</u> and add the numbers together.

You can also count the temperature change on a thermometer.

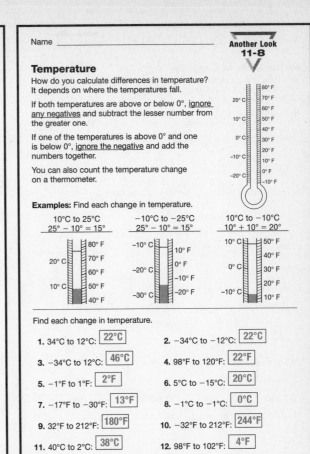

Examples: Find each change in temperature.

10°C to 25°C	−10°C to −25°C	10°C to −10°C
25° − 10° = 15°	25° − 10° = 15°	10° + 10° = 20°

Find each change in temperature.

1. 34°C to 12°C: [22°C]

2. −34°C to −12°C: [22°C]

3. −34°C to 12°C: [46°C]

4. 98°F to 120°F: [22°F]

5. −1°F to 1°F: [2°F]

6. 5°C to −15°C: [20°C]

7. −17°F to −30°F: [13°F]

8. −1°C to −1°C: [0°C]

9. 32°F to 212°F: [180°F]

10. −32°F to 212°F: [244°F]

11. 40°C to 2°C: [38°C]

12. 98°F to 102°F: [4°F]

146 Use with pages 504–505.

11-9 — Exploring Volume

Name _____

Another Look 11-9

Exploring Volume

In your book you used unit cubes to study volume. Here is another way to explore volume.

Length is the measure along one edge of a shape. *Area* measures a surface. *Volume* measures the space inside.

A box measures 12 in. long × 14 in. wide × 2 in. high.

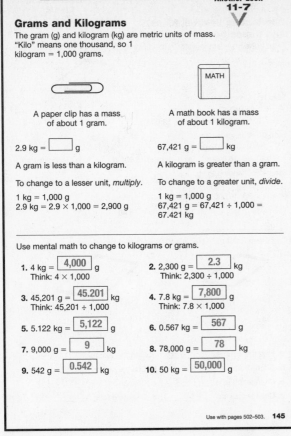

Its volume is the amount of space inside. By finding the product of the length, width, and height, you will find the number of 1-in. cubes that will fit in the box.

12 in. × 14 in. × 2 in. = 336 cubic inches, or 336 in³.
So, 336 1-in. cubes will fit in the box.

---

1. A water tank measures 15 ft long × 12 ft wide × 8 ft high.

Find the tank's volume. 15 ft × [12] ft × [8] ft = [1,440] ft³

2. A brick measures 30 cm long × 10 cm wide × 5 cm high.

   a. Find the brick's volume. ___1,500 cm³___

   b. How many 1-cm cubes would you have to glue together to make one brick with the same volume?
   ___1,500 1-cm cubes___

Find each volume.

3.
6 m, 2 m, 3 m
___36 m³___

4.
4 in., 16 in., 21 in.
___1,344 in³___

Use with pages 508–509. **147**

11-10 — Customary Units of Capacity

Name _____

Another Look 11-10

Customary Units of Capacity

Some people find it easier to change from one unit of capacity to another by converting the measurements to ounces first.

1 cup (c) = 8 fl oz
1 pint (pt) = 2 c = 16 fl oz
1 quart (qt) = 2 pt = 32 fl oz
1 gallon (gal) = 4 qt = 128 fl oz

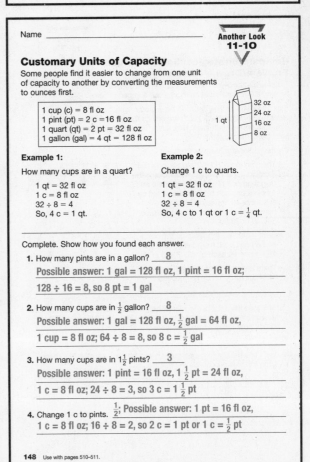

Example 1:

How many cups are in a quart?

1 qt = 32 fl oz
1 c = 8 fl oz
32 ÷ 8 = 4
So, 4 c = 1 qt.

Example 2:

Change 1 c to quarts.

1 qt = 32 fl oz
1 c = 8 fl oz
32 ÷ 8 = 4
So, 4 c to 1 qt or 1 c = ¼ qt.

Complete. Show how you found each answer.

1. How many pints are in a gallon? ___8___
Possible answer: 1 gal = 128 fl oz, 1 pint = 16 fl oz;
128 ÷ 16 = 8, so 8 pt = 1 gal

2. How many cups are in ½ gallon? ___8___
Possible answer: 1 gal = 128 fl oz, ½ gal = 64 fl oz,
1 cup = 8 fl oz; 64 ÷ 8 = 8, so 8 c = ½ gal

3. How many cups are in 1½ pints? ___3___
Possible answer: 1 pint = 16 fl oz, 1½ pt = 24 fl oz,
1 c = 8 fl oz; 24 ÷ 8 = 3, so 3 c = 1½ pt

4. Change 1 c to pints. ___½___; Possible answer: 1 pt = 16 fl oz,
1 c = 8 fl oz; 16 ÷ 8 = 2, so 2 c = 1 pt or 1 c = ½ pt

148 Use with pages 510–511.

201

Metric Units of Capacity

When changing from milliliters (mL) to liters (L), or liters to milliliters, just move the decimal point. Use zeros as "placeholders."

To change from mL to L, you have to divide by 1,000. So, move the decimal point 3 places to the left.

350 mL → 350. → 0.35 L

35 mL → 035. → 0.035 L

To change from L to mL, you have to multiply by 1,000. So, move the decimal point 3 places to the right.

4.5 L → 4.500 → 4,500 mL

0.045 L → 0.045 → 45 mL

Change each measurement to liters.

1. 1,700 mL = __1.7__ L   **2.** 170 mL = __0.17__ L

3. 17 mL = __0.017__ L   **4.** 50,000 mL = __50__ L

5. 3,950 mL = __3.95__ L   **6.** 625 mL = __0.625__ L

Change each measurement to milliliters.

7. 0.089 L = __89__ mL   **8.** 0.89 L = __890__ mL

9. 8.9 L = __8,900__ mL   **10.** 6.375 L = __6,375__ mL

11. 0.145 L = __145__ mL   **12.** 0.5 L = __500__ mL

Connecting Volume, Mass, and Capacity

What is the mass of the water in the aquarium?

Step 1 Find the volume.

20 cm × 20 cm × 40 cm = 16,000 cm³

Step 2 Change cm³ to mL.

1 cm³ holds 1 mL.
So, 16,000 cm³ holds 16,000 mL.

Step 3 Change mL to g.

1 mL of water has a mass of 1 g.
So, 16,000 mL has a mass of 16,000 g.

Step 4 Change g to kg.

1 kg = 1,000 g
So, 16,000 g = 16,000 ÷ 1,000 = 16 kg.

The mass of the water in the aquarium is 16 kg.

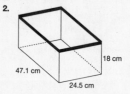

1 cm
(holds 1 ml)

Find the mass of the water in each aquarium in kilograms.

1.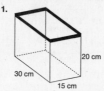
20 cm
30 cm
15 cm

2.
18 cm
47.1 cm
24.5 cm

a. Find the volume. __9,000 cm³__   **a.** Find the volume. __20771.1 cm³__

b. Change cm³ to mL. __9,000 mL__   **b.** Change cm³ to mL. __20771.1 mL__

c. Change mL to g. __9,000 g__   **c.** Change mL to g. __20771.1 g__

d. Change g to kg. __9 kg__   **d.** Change g to kg. __20.7711 kg__

Compare Strategies: Solve a Simpler Problem/Draw a Picture

Pictures can help you "see" a situation and solve a problem. Solving a Simpler Problem lets you use number patterns.

Rick and Charlie's neighborhood is 7 blocks long by 7 blocks wide. Each block has 8 houses on the north side and 8 houses on the south side. How many houses are in the neighborhood altogether?

Strategy: Solve a Simpler Problem

- The neighborhood is 7 blocks long and 7 blocks wide. There are 49 blocks in the neighborhood (7 × 7 = 49). If there was 1 house on each block, there would be 1 × 49 or 49 houses. If there were 2 houses on each block, there would be 2 × 49 or 98 houses.

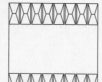

- Each block has 8 houses on the north and 8 houses on the south. There are 16 houses on each block. (8 + 8 = 16)

- There are 16 houses on each block, so there are 49 × 16, or 784 houses.

---

1. Suppose the neighborhood was only 5 blocks long and 5 blocks wide. If each block had 8 houses on the north side and 8 houses on the south, how many houses are there?

__400__

2. Lynn created the following pattern with beads. Draw the 25th bead Lynn will use to continue the pattern.

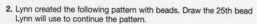

3. Lydia finished her math test after Sean but before Emily. Jane finished the test right after Sean. Mark finished last. Who finished first?

__Sean__

Ratios

A ratio is a pair of numbers that is used to compare quantities. The order in which you show the numbers is important.

You can write the ratio of hearts to squares. There are 2 hearts to 3 squares.

2 hearts and 3 squares
↓   ↓
2   to   3

You can also write the ratio as 2:3 or $\frac{2}{3}$.

You can also write the ratio of squares to hearts.

3 squares and 2 hearts
↓   ↓
3   to   2

This ratio can also be written as __3:2__ or $\frac{3}{2}$.

Write the ratio for the objects in each picture in 3 ways.

	Words	With a Colon	Fraction
1. diamonds to hearts	1 to 2	1:2	$\frac{1}{2}$
2. circles to squares	3 to 4	3:4	$\frac{3}{4}$
3. frowns to smiles	3 to 3 or 1 to 1	3:3 or 1:1	$\frac{3}{3}$ or $\frac{1}{1}$

Patterns in Ratio Tables

Two ratios that give the same comparison are called equal ratios.

For example, $\frac{1}{3}$ and $\frac{2}{6}$ are equal ratios.
Equal ratios can be thought of as equivalent fractions.

You can use what you know about fractions to find equal ratios. You can multiply or divide the numerator and denominator of a fraction by the same number to find equal ratios.

$\frac{1}{3} = \frac{1 \times 3}{3 \times 3} = \frac{3}{9}$ $\frac{3}{9} = \frac{3 \div 3}{9 \div 3} = \frac{1}{3}$

You can also use a ratio table to find equal ratios

1	2	3	4	7	10
3	6	9	12	21	30

1. Which pairs of ratios are equal? __B, C__

A. $\frac{2}{3}$ $\frac{4}{9}$ **B.** $\frac{3}{5}$ $\frac{6}{10}$ **C.** $\frac{2}{4}$ $\frac{1}{2}$ **D.** $\frac{3}{8}$ $\frac{9}{16}$

Complete the fractions to make equal ratios.

2. $\frac{2}{5} = \frac{4}{\boxed{10}} = \frac{\boxed{6}}{15}$ **3.** $\frac{8}{28} = \frac{4}{\boxed{14}} = \frac{\boxed{2}}{7}$

Complete each ratio table.

4.
2	4	6
5	10	15

5.
8	4	2
28	14	7

Exploring Equal Ratios

In your book you found equal ratios. Here is another way to find if ratios are equal.

Show the ratios as fractions. Write the fractions in their simplest form. If they match, they are equal ratios.

Are $\frac{2}{4}$, $\frac{4}{8}$, $\frac{8}{16}$, and $\frac{16}{32}$ equal ratios?

$\frac{2}{4} = \frac{1}{2}$ $\frac{4}{8} = \frac{1}{2}$

$\frac{8}{16} = \frac{1}{2}$ $\frac{16}{32} = \frac{1}{2}$

Yes, they are equal ratios because each one can be written as $\frac{1}{2}$.

1. Are $\frac{2}{6}$, $\frac{4}{12}$, $\frac{6}{18}$, and $\frac{8}{24}$ equal ratios? How do you know?

Yes, they are equal ratios because each one can be written as $\frac{1}{3}$.

Each ratio on the left is matched by 4 ratios on the right. One of the ratios on the right is not equal to the one on the left. Find the one that is not equal. Write it on the line.

2. $\frac{2}{3}$ $\frac{4}{6}$ $\frac{3}{12}$ $\frac{6}{10}$ $\frac{3}{15}$ $\frac{3}{6}$

3. $\frac{1}{5}$ $\frac{3}{15}$ $\frac{5}{15}$ $\frac{2}{10}$ $\frac{6}{30}$ $\frac{5}{15}$

4. $\frac{1}{4}$ $\frac{9}{27}$ $\frac{9}{36}$ $\frac{7}{28}$ $\frac{6}{24}$ $\frac{9}{27}$

5. $\frac{3}{4}$ $\frac{75}{100}$ $\frac{9}{12}$ $\frac{6}{8}$ $\frac{8}{16}$ $\frac{8}{16}$

6. $\frac{2}{5}$ $\frac{6}{15}$ $\frac{8}{20}$ $\frac{10}{25}$ $\frac{12}{30}$ $\frac{5}{25}$

7. $\frac{1}{3}$ $\frac{3}{7}$ $\frac{3}{9}$ $\frac{4}{12}$ $\frac{5}{15}$ $\frac{3}{7}$

8. $\frac{3}{8}$ $\frac{9}{24}$ $\frac{6}{16}$ $\frac{12}{32}$ $\frac{21}{40}$ $\frac{21}{40}$

Decision Making

Your scout troop is planning a kickball day. You decide to make a scale drawing of the field area on grid paper to help you plan for the event. The drawing will be proportional to the actual field area.

Some Facts

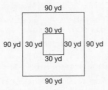

• The entire field is a square, 90 yards on each side.
• The kickball field is a smaller square in the middle that measures 30 yards on each side.

Here are some questions you can ask when you are figuring out dimensions for a scale drawing.

How many yards could 1 square show?
90 and 30 are each divisible by 3, 6, 10, and 15.
Each square could show a length of __3 yd__, __6 yd__, __10 yd__, or __15 yd__.

How many squares show one side of the big field?
Suppose each square shows 3 yards.
90 ÷ 3 = __30__, so 30 squares are needed for each side.

How many squares show one side of the kickball field?
Suppose each square shows 3 yards.
30 ÷ 3 = __10__, so 10 squares are needed for each side.

1. Suppose each square shows 10 yards.
How many squares show one side of the big field? __9 squares__

The kickball field? __3 squares__

2. Suppose each square shows 15 yards.
How many squares show one side of the big field? __6 squares__

The kickball field? __2 squares__

Exploring Percent Patterns

In your book you learned how to use patterns to find percents. Here is another way to understand percent patterns.

• All of the fractions in the same column below are equivalent.
• Equivalent fractions are equal to the same percent.

5%	10%	15%	20%	25%	30%
$\frac{5}{100}$	$\frac{10}{100}$	$\frac{15}{100}$	$\frac{20}{100}$	$\frac{25}{100}$	$\frac{30}{100}$
$\frac{1}{20}$	$\frac{2}{20}$	$\frac{3}{20}$	$\frac{4}{20}$	$\frac{5}{20}$	$\frac{6}{20}$
	$\frac{1}{10}$		$\frac{2}{10}$		$\frac{3}{10}$
			$\frac{1}{5}$		
				$\frac{1}{4}$	

Which fractions are equal to 10%? $\frac{10}{100}, \frac{2}{20}, \frac{1}{10}$

Which fractions are equal to 25%? $\frac{25}{100}, \frac{5}{20}, \frac{1}{4}$

You know $\frac{1}{20} = 5\%$. What percent does $\frac{4}{20}$ equal?

$4 \times \frac{1}{20} = \frac{4}{20}$ and $4 \times 5\% = 20\%$ so, $\frac{4}{20} = $ __20%__.

1. Which fractions are equal to 15%? $\frac{15}{100}, \frac{3}{20}$

2. Which fractions are equal to 20%? $\frac{20}{100}, \frac{4}{20}, \frac{2}{10}, \frac{1}{5}$

3. What percent does each fraction equal?

a. $\frac{5}{100}$ __5%__   **b.** $\frac{20}{100}$ __20%__   **c.** $\frac{40}{100}$ __40%__

d. $\frac{3}{4}$ __75%__   **e.** $\frac{3}{5}$ __60%__   **f.** $\frac{5}{10}$ __50%__

Another Look
12-6

Estimating Percent of a Number

The chart below shows when you might use each benchmark percent when estimating percents.

Problem	To Use Benchmarks	Estimates
11% of 110	10% or $\frac{1}{10}$	10% of 110 is <u>11</u>
24% of 800	25% or $\frac{1}{4}$	25% of 800 is <u>200</u>
35% of 270	$33\frac{1}{3}$% or $\frac{1}{3}$	$33\frac{1}{3}$% of 270 is <u>90</u>
46% of 301	50% or $\frac{1}{2}$	50% of 300 is <u>150</u>
62% of 17	$66\frac{2}{3}$% or $\frac{2}{3}$	$66\frac{2}{3}$% of 18 is <u>12</u>
77% of 46	75% or $\frac{3}{4}$	75% of 48 is <u>36</u>

Write the percent benchmark you would use to estimate.

1. 76% of 180 <u>75%</u>   2. 32% of 33 <u>$33\frac{1}{3}$%</u>   3. 46% of 320 <u>50%</u>

4. 9% of 20 <u>10%</u>   5. 63% of 150 <u>$66\frac{2}{3}$%</u>   6. 22% of 80 <u>25%</u>

Estimate. **Possible estimates are given.**

7. 37% of 36 <u>about 12</u>   8. 28% of 41 <u>about 10 or 12</u>

9. 52% of 47 <u>about 23 or 24</u>   10. 71% of 19 <u>about 15</u>

11. 68% of 23 <u>about 16</u>   12. 9% of 24 <u>about 2</u>

Another Look
12-7

Finding Percent of a Number

Follow the three examples to learn ways to find 30% of $40.

Example 1

1. Change 30% to a decimal .

$$30\% = 30 \div 100 = 0.30$$

2. Multiply $40 and 0.30.

$$\begin{array}{r} \$4\,0 \\ \times\quad 0.3\,0 \\ \hline \$1\,2.0\,0 \end{array}$$

Example 2

1. Change 30% to a fraction in simplest form.

$$30\% = 30 \div 100 = \frac{30}{100} = \frac{3}{10}$$

2. Multiply. $\frac{3}{10} \times \$40 = \frac{\$120}{10} = \underline{\$12}$

Example 3

Use a calculator. Press 30 % × 40 = ☐ 12

Complete to find the percent of each.

1. 45% of 25

 a. $45 \div 100 = $ ☐ 0.45

 b. ☐ 0.45 $\times 25 = $ ☐ 11.25

2. 18% of 55

 a. $18 \div$ ☐ 100 $= 0.18$

 b. ☐ 0.18 $\times$ ☐ 55 $= $ 9.9

3. 22% of 150

 a. $22\% = \frac{22}{100} = $ ☐$\frac{11}{50}$

 b. ☐$\frac{11}{50} \times 150 = $ ☐$\frac{1,650}{50} = $ ☐ 33

4. 32% of 175

 a. $32\% = $ ☐$\frac{32}{100} = $ ☐$\frac{8}{25}$

 b. ☐$\frac{8}{25} \times 175 = $ ☐$\frac{1,400}{25} = $ ☐ 56

Choose a method. Find the percent of each.

5. 40% of 120 <u>48</u>   6. 70% of 210 <u>147</u>

7. 60% of 185 <u>111</u>   8. 75% of 500 <u>375</u>

9. 80% of 400 <u>320</u>   10. 20% of 360 <u>72</u>

Another Look
12-8

Exploring Fairness

In your book you explored fairness by playing a game. Here is another way to understand fairness.

Joe and Larry take turns spinning the spinner. Joe scores one point if the spinner lands on R. Larry scores one point if the spinner lands on G. Is this a fair game?

The outcomes possible are R and G. Each outcome has the same size space on the spinner, so each is equally likely to occur.

The game is <u>fair</u>.

In a second game, Joe and Larry use another spinner but keep the same rules.

The outcomes possible are R and G. It is more likely that they will spin R than G since the R area is larger than the G area. The outcomes are not equally likely.

The game is <u>unfair</u>.

Tell if the outcome is fair or unfair.

If unfair, tell which outcome is more likely.

1. Draw a name out of the hat.
   <u>unfair; more likely to draw Tom</u>

2. Spin the spinner.
   <u>fair</u>

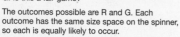

3. Choose a marble from the bowl.
   <u>fair</u>

Another Look
12-9

Exploring Predicting from Samples

In your book you explored predictions by doing a letter tally. Here is another way to explore predictions.

A sample is a small set taken from a large set. Predictions can be made about the large set by looking at the sample set.

There are 200 red, green, yellow, and blue marbles in a box. How many red marbles do you predict are in the box?

Follow the steps to find out.

Step 1   Without looking, take a sample of 20 marbles out of the box.

Step 2   Count the number of red marbles in the sample. Suppose there are 8 red marbles.

Step 3   Make a ratio and solve.

red marbles in sample → $\frac{8}{20} = \frac{n}{200}$ ← red marbles in bag
total marbles in sample →   ← total marbles in bag

Use equivalent fractions to solve.

$\frac{8 \times 10}{20 \times 10} = \frac{80}{200}$

You predict there will be <u>80</u> red marbles in the box of 200 marbles.

1. In a sample, 5 out of 20 marbles are yellow. Predict how many yellow marbles are in a box of 100 marbles.
   <u>25</u>

2. In a sample, 11 out of 25 marbles are green. Predict how many green marbles are in a box of 100 marbles.
   <u>44</u>

3. In a sample, 9 out of 50 marbles are blue. Predict how many blue marbles are in a box of 400 marbles.
   <u>72</u>

4. In a sample, 12 out of 100 marbles are black. Predict how many black marbles are in a box of 300 marbles.
   <u>36</u>

Exploring Predicting from Experiments

In your book you used coins to explore predicting. Here is another way to understand predictions.

You can predict the outcome you expect to happen when you spin the spinner.

If you spin the spinner 9 times, how many times do you predict the outcome will be B?

The spinner is equally likely to land on R, B, or G.

Since there are 3 equal outcomes, 1 out of every 3 spins should be B.

$\frac{1 \times 3}{3 \times 3} = \frac{3}{9}$ __3__ out of every 9 spins should be B.

To see if your predictions are correct, you can experiment by spinning the spinner and recording the results in a table. The more times the experiment is performed, the closer the results will be to the predicted outcomes.

1. Each face of the number cube has one of the numbers 1, 2, 3, 4, 5, or 6. In 20 tosses, how many times do you expect an even number to be rolled?

__10__

2. Toss the number cube 20 times. Complete the tally table.

Check students' work

Outcome	Tally	Total	Outcome	Tally	Total
1			4		
2			5		
3			6		

3. Did the experiment support your prediction?

Answer may be yes, although 20 tosses may not be enough to support the prediction.

Analyze Strategies: Make an Organized List

A diner has a platter special of one meat and one vegetable for $2.99. You have a choice of 3 meats and 4 vegetables. How many choices are there for the platter?

Platter Special	
1 Meat	1 Vegetable
beef	spinach
pork	asparagus
chicken	zucchini
	egg plant

You can find out by making an organized list. A tree diagram is one way to make an organized list.

Choose a letter for each meat and vegetable. Match each meat with each of the vegetables.

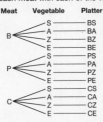

Count the number of platters. There are __12__.

Use a tree diagram to solve the problem.

The school cafeteria serves sandwiches. You can choose ham, salami, or turkey, on whole wheat, rye, or 7-grain bread. How many sandwich combinations are there?

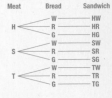

9; answers will vary for tree diagram. Possible tree diagram shown.

Expressing Probabilities as Fractions

The spinner is divided into 8 equal parts.

There are 8 possible outcomes. Since 3 parts have the letter C, 3 of the 8 outcomes are C's. The probability of the spinner stopping on C is 3 out of 8 or $\frac{3}{8}$.

Two out of the 8 possible outcomes are B's, so the probability of stopping on B is $\frac{2}{8}$, or in simplest form, $\frac{1}{4}$.

The probability of stopping on A is __2__ out of 8, or $\frac{2}{8}$ or $\frac{1}{4}$.

The probability of stopping on D is __1__ out of 8, or $\frac{1}{8}$.

Give the probability of each outcome as a fraction. Simplify.

1. What is the probability the spinner will stop on

a. R? $\frac{1}{2}$

b. B? $\frac{1}{3}$

c. Y? $\frac{1}{6}$

2. Toss a cube with these faces. What is the probability of rolling

a. a triangle? $\frac{1}{2}$

b. a circle? $\frac{1}{3}$

c. a square? $\frac{1}{6}$

Exploring Expected and Experimental Results

The spinner is divided into 4 equal parts. There are 4 equally likely possible outcomes.

So the probability of each of the 4 outcomes is $\frac{1}{4}$.

Suppose the spinner is spun 20 times.

To find the **expected results** for getting A in 20 spins, multiply the probability of getting A by the number of spins.

$\frac{1}{4} \times 20 =$ __5__

You should expect to get A, 5 times.

For each spinner, find the probability for the outcome. Then find the expected results.

1. Outcome: 2

Probability: $\frac{1}{2}$

Expected results for 50 spins:

$\frac{1}{2} \times 50 =$ __25__

2. Outcome: C

Probability: $\frac{1}{3}$

Expected results for 90 spins:

$\frac{1}{3} \times 90 =$ __30__